Plants That Changed the World

LITTLE, BROWN & COMPANY

BOSTON   TORONTO

PLANTS
THAT CHANGED
THE WORLD

by

BERTHA S. DODGE
Illustrated by HENRY B. KANE

The author is grateful to Henry Holt and Company, Inc., for permission
to quote briefly from WHITE WATER AND BLACK MAGIC by Richard C. Gill.

Published simultaneously in Canada
by Little, Brown & Company (Canada) Limited

PRINTED IN THE UNITED STATES OF AMERICA

Foreword

C490028

OUR MINDS are so full of the wonders performed in synthetic laboratories that we are apt to let ourselves believe men invented the idea of chemical synthesis. Actually the laboratory workers are often doing little more than copying plants. Plants made the first fibers that men twisted into ropes — and a world without ropes is almost unimaginable. Plants first synthesized drugs, and are still busy making a long list that includes such essentials as penicillin and quinine. Plants started the billion-dollar business of elastomers and plastics. Most important of all, plants have taught men how to copy their products in the laboratory.

It is not hard to see that chemists would have had few such plant products to study had there not first been other men to study the plants themselves. These men — botanists and plant collectors — though too rarely acknowledged, leave us permanently in their debt. Without their careful science, without their knowledge of plants and their willingness to go anywhere in pursuit of them, we could not have brought some of our most vital plants into cultivation and secured their products in quantities sufficient to keep pace with ever increasing demand. That chemists have sometimes managed to improve upon the natural products does not in any way lessen the importance of the plants or of their collectors.

This book is an attempt to describe some of the plant products that have helped make history. Naturally, we must focus our attention upon the men who sought the plants in remote wildernesses and brought them back for less adventurous men to use.

Adventurous as plant hunting has always been, hunting for plant hunters and their stories has offered adventure of its own. If a valuable plant is of ancient use, the history of its discovery and introduction into cultivation may well be lost in the mists of ages. A plant whose importance is of recent recognition may be a sort of trade secret. Plant hunters sent out by commercial houses are not always at liberty to discuss their findings and adventures. And many men do not take time or find words to tell others about what seems to them to be a quite routine life.

In this book, I have deliberately left out all discussion of ornamental plants and of their hunters — who happen to be among the most articulate plant collectors. The bibliography at the end will give a partial idea of the reading done. It includes some titles that may be difficult to locate and many that should be met with in larger libraries. It does not, of course, include every work consulted.

I must acknowledge my indebtedness to many patient librarians, too numerous to list by name. Specific acknowledgment must be given Mr. William A. Scherff, Advertising and Sales Promotion Manager of the Plymouth Cordage Company of Plymouth, Massachusetts. Mr. Scherff not only took time to answer any questions I wished to ask about the history and use of abacá fiber but sent me his Company's *Manual of Rope Usage* as a gift and loaned me a copy of the now out of print book, Dr. Morison's *The Ropemakers of Plymouth*.

Most of the quotations in this book are from long out of print books or from government publications. One exception is Mr. Richard Gill's fascinating account of his pursuit of the ingredients of curare, *White Water and Black Magic,* published by Henry Holt & Company. I am deeply indebted to these publishers for permission to include the specific passages quoted.

BERTHA S. DODGE

Contents

BOOKS BY BERTHA S. DODGE

Introduction to Chemistry

The Story of Nursing

Plants That Changed the World

Plants That Changed the World

TO CARROLL

who made known to me the delights of plant hunting

I

Lilacs and Lilies

THROUGHOUT THE AGES, when men have moved their homes from one land to another, they have taken with them their most prized possessions, their domestic animals, and seeds or cuttings of their favorite garden plants. Where they settle, homes are built, cattle graze, and their plants take root. When again they move on, these men must leave behind both the homes and the growing plants, though their cattle, being as rootless as their masters, can move on too. The empty houses fall into disuse and decay. Wind and weather lay them low.

And what of the plants? The hardier ones, like our familiar apple trees, cast their seed far and wide over the earth to breed a multitude of disreputable wild offspring. But the plants which form no living seeds, whose only method of propagation is by spreading roots, cannot move far. Year after year, they spring up loyally in the spot where they were planted, to grow and flower and bear mute testimony to forgotten homesites.

Seek out, in the remoter areas of New Hampshire or Vermont, traces of abandoned country roads. Encroaching shrubs and trees have long since obliterated the wheel tracks. Yet, if you know how to look, you may still find the broken lines of lichen-covered stones that once belonged to neatly laid roadside walls. Walk between these and you will come, perhaps, to further evidence of man's onetime dwelling — a family cemetery, its headstones tilted crazily or completely overthrown by pasturing cattle and by the swelling roots of forest trees. Only an expert eye will recognize the spot, and even that eye will be unable to decipher the weathered epitaphs.

But no eye can miss nearby the living testimony to past human habitation — the great spreading clumps of tough-stemmed lilacs and the masses of slender pointed leaves where, in season, a riot of flame-colored day lilies proudly marks the former residence of men.

Yet why accept the testimony of just these two plants out of the thousands crowding in upon the clearing? The answer is simple. Because they, like the men who brought them and set them out, are aliens in the land. The lilac — *Syringa persica,* to assign its botanical name — traces its ancestry to far-away Persia. Relatives of the day lily are native on the cold upper slopes of towering tropical mountains. Except as they grow in their remote native habitats, such plants testify undeniably to men's presence. Where they are, men have been; where men have not been, they cannot be.

Thus, out of the frail materials of which plant tissues are composed, men have raised themselves monuments more enduring than the stones from which frost and rain have long since erased the inscriptions. Monuments not only to the men and women whose dooryards they marked, they bring to mind those equally forgotten men of long ago who looked upon alien plants, found them good or beautiful, and bore home cuttings from which multitudes of new plants might spring in the far places of the earth. They remind us, too, of the debt we of today owe to plants and to the plant hunters of more recent times.

Wherever there is plant life — from microscopic bacteria to great trees — simple raw materials are being put together into complex products of manufacture: foodstuffs, fibers, fuels, drugs. And unlike man-built factories, plant factories waste very little either of the raw materials or of the energy required to convert them into manufactured products.

For a long time, nonscientific agricultural men had to depend almost completely upon plant products. Even when they ate animal flesh or spun and wove animal fibers, or burned animal fats like tallow and whale oil, they were still, though indirectly, relying upon the plants that had nourished and kept the animals alive. Neither men nor animals are endowed with that power, so essential to life, of taking nitrogen directly from the air and converting it into the proteins needed for tissue building. They have to get these proteins from food plants which, in turn, rely upon still smaller plants — certain bacteria that have the ability to take the gas, nitrogen, from the air and fix it in usable form. Even costly synthetic fertilizers are of little direct value to us. Until plants have done their bit, we are helpless.

As civilizations have developed and men's needs grown increasingly complicated, the simple plants of yesteryear have ceased to satisfy all these needs. Though men have moved further and further from the agricultural life, their dependence upon plants has increased. The progress of civilization is marked by the discovery of new plant products — like rubber, for instance — and by finding new uses for old, like the wood fibers from which cellulose products such as acetates and rayons and explosives are prepared. And still the supply of such products cannot keep up with the demand.

Nonagricultural man must turn with new understanding and enthusiasm to the old study of plants. May there not be new plant varieties which can produce more or better types of the old products? May there not be in still undiscovered plants properties with values as yet undreamed of? A drug, perhaps, or an antibiotic to deal with some of men's most baffling diseases? You never can tell . . .

Where might they come from — these new plant products? Occasionally and rarely from our own doorsteps, as when green leaves from spinach or alfalfa or even weeds are used to prepare Vitamin K which helps blood coagulation and thus may stop hemorrhages. Undoubtedly we would have many more such products than we have if we only knew where to look for them. We can hardly pick up any strange herb and say, "This I will use for a cancer cure." Or "The bark of this tree will bring relief to my headaches." We know all too well that the cancer cure might prove worthless or deadly and the headache remedy could well put an end to all possibility of future headaches.

Of all the useful plants that have come to us out of the wilderness, none are more fascinating or more baffling than the drug plants. How could they have been discovered? How was it possible for any man to select from the thousands of plants that grew all around him the one plant whose fruit or bark or roots contained a cure specific for his own special kind of illness? And how did he ever solve the delicate question of effective dosage?

Reason answers coolly, "He couldn't."

Fact tells, undeniably, "He did."

Moreover the wild untutored forest dwellers did it not once but over and over again. Modern men of medicine are humble before their unscientific colleagues, the medicine men. Today medical scientists are willing to give unbiased tests, at least, to the ancient folk remedies which their predecessors scorned. Today plant hunters will find and bring back material for these tests if it is humanly possible. All they need is clues.

What kind of clues? Well, perhaps some ancient legend tells of a long-forgotten king cured of an incurable disease. Perhaps an unexpected modern cure is related to a persistent folk tale passed from one generation to another through uncounted ages. It need be only a vague hint dropped in a receptive ear: the natives of such and such a remote village claim they can cure those recurring chills and fevers by chewing the bark of certain trees; the oil prepared from bark or fruit of another tree has actually cured leprosy—we've seen it with our own eyes. Or, there's a tree up the Amazon with a sticky sap that dries into the strangest elastic material. Just a few words and the right ear, and presently the plant hunter sets forth in search of something — he may not know precisely what or just where he may hope to encounter it.

What qualities make the professional plant hunter? What

are the reasons that take a highly educated man out of the comfortable routine of civilized life to send him seeking across the world for something he can have no certainty of finding? The answer probably lies in that important quality called scientific curiosity.

"What," the scientist asks himself, "can I learn from plants? What gaps in human knowledge can I hope to fill?"

Perhaps, as in past centuries, the answer will seem to hold no immediate interest for anyone except the kind of botanist who agonizes over assigning the correct name to a plant which he has seen only as a dried specimen laid between sheets of paper in a museum called an "herbarium."

So, our botanist writes an impressive epitaph like *"Taraktogenos kurzii"* beside the brittle, lifeless specimen and lays it to rest, along with thousands of other plants, in tall cases. He probably forgets about it. Probably everyone else does too. And then, years later, the echo of some ancient legend may raise the faded specimen out of its tomb.

"The kalaw tree?" our botanist murmurs. "Thought to be the same as *Taraktogenos kurzii?* Yes, I believe we have a specimen from the forests of northeastern India — the characters are quite clear . . ." And the hunt is on.

A plant hunter should, of course, have training in the classification of plants so that he can recognize the special one he is seeking when he meets it. He should be able to recognize related species and bring them back, too, if he can; they also might be manufacturing useful plant products. Moreover, the hunter should have an instinct for spotting ornamental or useful plants beyond those which are the object of his special search. They might justify the time and expense of his trip should he fail to attain his prime objective. Of course he must be able to prepare collections of dried specimens so that plant hunters of the future may find help in them.

The plant hunter has to take all sorts of physical hardships in his stride and must be able to endure long periods far from the cheering warmth of human companionship. Yet he had better be able to get along with people — his backers, should he be fortunate enough to have them; government officials of the lands he hopes to explore and whose consent he must win before starting out into the wilds. Most of all, he must be able to win the friendship or, at the very least, quiet the suspicions of the residents of the immediate areas he will be working in. Since the days of Sir Joseph Banks plant hunters, in their native lands, have been mistaken for bandits or spies. In lands where they are aliens, they can expect even worse receptions if they are not careful. To have to plead their causes in a foreign tongue, hundreds of miles from counsel, before antagonistic judges who are themselves the law and who neither know nor care that they may be dealing with distinguished scientists — this is a prospect far more chilling than pursuit by a tiger. The tiger can be shot without argument and his death will bring no crises in its wake.

II

Joseph Banks
and the Breadfruit

THERE WAS NOTHING about fourteen-year-old Joseph Banks
— so his Eton tutor told himself — that set the lad apart from
most of his schoolmates. Not a blockhead, not a distinguished
student, perhaps a shade too fond of games and sports, young
Joseph could in due time be expected to settle down upon his
inherited estate of Revesby Abbey in Lincolnshire and become

the typical narrow country gentleman of his day. It would be enough, of course, yet the tutor wished it might be more.

Then, one day, the startled tutor came upon his young charge hungrily reading a book that, even from a distance, the tutor could see was not required reading. He smiled happily, thinking, after the manner of teachers of any land or age, "At last I have made an impression on the lad! Maybe he'll amount to something yet."

Had the tutor known the exact nature of the book Joseph Banks was reading, he would have despaired more than ever of the lad's future. Imagine a student at Eton in the year 1758 wasting time on an herbal — a book about plants, of all things! Such a book might be suitable enough for Joseph's mother and aunts. Flowers were a proper interest for women. But for a youth destined for a high place in society — and one who had not yet made serious effort to master the subjects any well-brought-up young man should know — never! The tutor would have shuddered in horror at the very idea.

In 1758 the study of plants had little place in courses of study of either preparatory schools or universities. Science was still a poor relation of the arts — necessary for future medical practitioners but scarcely to be regarded as a part of any non-professional course of study. Classics, literature, history — the well-educated youth must have a nodding acquaintance with these so that he might be able to talk easily and wittily in the luxurious London drawing rooms. But botany! Why, it was scarcely to be preferred to farming! To a tutor brought up in the strict classical tradition, the idea must be wildly and dangerously unconventional.

Tutors notwithstanding, Joseph Banks had already determined to devote his life to the study of plants. He knew that he was defying established educational conventions. He could hardly foresee, though, that he was setting his feet upon strange, perilous, fascinating paths that would presently lead him to the remote fastnesses of the then incompletely charted globe. Nor could he foresee his lasting influence upon other botanists who would follow in his footsteps — some to fame, some to shame, some never to return to the land of their birth. And when a century or more had passed and Joseph Banks was long since laid in his grave, men who had scarcely heard mention of Sir Joseph Banks would still be setting out on quests inspired by the man's inextinguishable enthusiasm for natural history.

It began on a warm summer's evening in 1758 when a group of young Eton students went together for a swim in a neighboring river. Slower than the others in leaving the water and in putting on his clothes, Joseph saw them disappearing in the distance by the time he was ready to start home. He found he did not mind being alone. With no schoolmates at hand to taunt him and call him "sissy," he could linger as he chose and look his fill at the masses of wild flowers that bloomed along the path. As the long rays of the setting sun touched them with an almost unearthly beauty, he became suddenly and urgently aware of an inner need to know more about them. Impulsively, but unshakably, he decided to devote his life to study of plants.

But how, he asked himself. Not at Eton. Must he then wait until he reached the university? He found his answer in a group of old village women. The wrinkled crones gathered herbs and "simples" — medicinal plants — to sell to the village apothecary. They were ignorant women. Joseph knew they couldn't either read or write, but they had what was to him an infinitely precious store of wisdom. They could call each plant by name and recognize its use and value.

Might they, he wondered eagerly, be persuaded to share this knowledge? Joseph Banks, youth or old man, rarely failed to persuade people to do what he wanted. The crones agreed to teach the inquisitive lad what they knew about plants and he agreed to pay them sixpence a lesson. Fortunately word of this arrangement never came to his Eton tutor's ears.

In Revesby Abbey during his next holidays, Joseph came upon an impressive book resting on a table in his mother's dressing room. Gerard's *Herball* it was — one of those books that told the names of flowers and herbs and gave their uses, decorative, practical, or medicinal. It also contained a number of beautifully and intricately hand-colored plates from which ladies of those times loved to draw patterns for their elaborate needlepoint embroideries. The book was an appropriate addition to a lady's dressing room.

To the lady's son, it looked like the answer to a prayer. He bore it off to his own room where he eagerly began devouring its contents. It went back with him to Eton after the holidays. There his tutor found him reading it.

Two years later young Banks went up to Oxford University. To his dismay, he found that Oxford had little more to offer in the way of botanical education than had Eton. But Cambridge University, he knew, had a more alert interest in natural sciences. Being a youth of independent means, he could afford a journey to Cambridge, seek out a man with botanical training, and bring that man back to Oxford with him. This man, Israel Lyons by name, agreed to teach botany to Joseph Banks and to such of his friends as might have an interest in the subject.

Undoubtedly it was Lyons who introduced Banks to the system of grouping and naming plants which the great Swedish botanist Linnaeus had recently developed and published. This

system was lifting the study of plants from the almost superstitious kind of knowledge possessed by the village crones to
the level of a science worthy to be ranked with the other young
and growing sciences of that day. In its main outlines, Linnaeus' system is still used today.

To some, the grouping and naming of plants may seem like
a dull kind of occupation. To Joseph Banks and his friends
it was always infinitely fascinating. Through this systematic
arrangements of plants, they could at last watch the great plan
of Nature become apparent, bit by bit. Always an adventure
of the mind, it might well become adventure of a far more
active kind.

If you pursue knowledge with your whole heart, you must
be ready to follow whithersoever it may lead you. If you spy a
new or interesting plant growing along the sides of a muddy
roadside ditch, you will collect it whatever the costs to dignity
or clothing. That was the way Joseph Banks felt about it and
the way he always acted. Later in life, at fashionable dinner
tables, an older Sir Joseph loved to shock his listeners with an
account of one such roadside adventure.

While the young botanist was happily inspecting the inside
of a ditch, on the road nearby an enterprising bandit held
up the coach of a gentleman of wealth. Naturally the officer of
the law who came upon the youth skulking in the ditch
thought he had found the robber. The magistrate was inclined
to agree, though the youth stoutly maintained his complete
innocence. This muddy rascal the heir to Revesby! Ridiculous!
Yet hadn't there been talk about young Banks's queer doings?
Better play safe and treat the youth courteously while his identity was checked.

People do not change a great deal through the centuries.
Even today enterprising botanists find themselves looked upon

with grave suspicion. Something is wrong with a guy who spends his life hunting plants — and you can't tell me he wouldn't be capable of almost anything! Imagine a normal grown man collecting weeds or lichens! Even in his own land, a botanist can find unexpected adventure.

As in Sir Joseph's day, though, the botanist finds adventure more frequently and more satisfyingly in exploring remote parts of the world. Before Sir Joseph's time, such exploration was quite rare. Only a real pioneer, an exceptionally bold and adventurous spirit and one completely devoted to his chosen pursuit, dared venture far afield into a world so wide that the farthest end of England — less than two hundred miles as the crow flies — was several days' journey from the capital. Yet the young Joseph would scheme and pull strings and use all the influence which social position and family connections afforded to get passage on cramped and uncomfortable sailing vessels setting out for the distant places of the earth.

Years later, the older and settled Sir Joseph would write his disapproval to a young botanist whose alarmed family had dissuaded him from undertaking botanical exploration in fever-ridden Java: "Let me hear from you how you feel inclined to prefer ease and indulgence to hardship and activity. I was about twenty-three when I began my peregrinations. You are somewhat older, but you may be assured that I had listened to a multitude of voices raised to dissuade, I would have been now a quiet country gentleman, ignorant of a number of things I am now acquainted with."

Ignorant — and poorer! Moving within narrow horizons, without entrancing memories of remote and beautiful parts of the earth or of its many peoples through whom he learned a wisdom and tolerance rare in any age! He would have known little of the curious and valuable plants of other lands; and as it turned out, not only Joseph Banks but the whole world might have been poorer had he "listened to a multitude of voices raised to dissuade" him.

In 1766 he made his first long trip as naturalist on a Fisheries Protection vessel bound for a seven months' cruise of the waters of Newfoundland and Labrador. A bold undertaking for a noble gentleman of those days, it gave him a taste of what such trips might mean in terms of monotony and discomfort. If he ever chafed at these, he was more than compensated by the large numbers of new plants he could collect during excursions ashore. On board, the work of pressing, drying, and labeling kept his hands full. He was laying the foundations of his own large personal herbarium.

On the return voyage the vessel called at the port of Lisbon in Portugal. There Banks first met that curious rarity from the New World, caoutchouc, presently to be called "India rubber." A century later, plant hunters in the great tradition which Banks had yet to found would be setting forth for remote Amazon jungles to bring back to England seeds of the tree which produced this caoutchouc. And when at long last the project would meet with success, those seeds would be planted in the Royal Botanic Gardens at Kew, of which Sir Joseph was the real organizer and first distinguished director.

The scientists of the highly science-conscious eighteenth century saw in young Joseph Banks a true kindred spirit. His courage, which did not let him shrink from travel in remote areas of the world, his curiosity wide as that world itself, his personal collection of books and of plant specimens — all pointed to him as a most suitable member of that great fellowship of scholars, the Royal Society. Soon after his return from Newfoundland he was elected a Fellow of the Society. More than an empty honor, this election made him a part of a stimulating group of alert and inquiring minds. It gave him a share in their plans and their visions.

One of the plans which the astronomers of the group were then furthering was to make accurate observations of the "Transit of Venus" — the passage of the planet Venus across the face of the sun — calculated to be visible on June 3, 1769. They felt that these observations should "contribute greatly to the improvement of Astronomy upon which Navigation so greatly depends." They felt, too, that to make observations of the event complete, one set should be recorded from an observation post in the South Seas. So "The President, Council and Fellows of the Royal Society for improving Natural Knowledge" made humble petition to His Majesty, the King, to give financial support to the projected costly expedition.

Of course the new Fellow could not fail to see in these plans an opportunity for his own science, botany. Why should not the chartered ship bear botanists as well as astronomers? It could not hinder observers of a distant planet to be associated with other men who were occupied with studying their own planet. Eagerly persuasive, Banks won the assent of the President and Council of the Royal Society. They sent their formal recommendation to the British Admiralty, under whose supervision arrangements for the voyage were being made: "Joseph Banks, Esq., Fellow of this Society, a gentleman of large fortune, who is well versed in Natural History, being desirous of undertaking the same voyage, the Council very urgently requests their Lordships, that in regard to Mr. Banks' great personal merit and for the advancement of useful knowledge, he also, together with his suite, being seven persons more (that is eight persons in all) together with their baggage, be received on board the ship under the command of Captain Cook."

Captain Cook! A name to conjure with! One of the greatest seamen and explorers of all time, Captain Cook would on this trip take the little bark *Endeavour* completely around the world. It required courage of no ordinary dimensions to undertake such a trip. Even under the most skilled of captains, the hazards would be great. They would sail stormy and uncharted seas. They would have to land, for watering and victualing, on shores that belonged to strange savages at whose doubtful mercy they might find themselves. A risk for all concerned — seamen, officers, naturalists — it was greatest for the captain. On his third voyage around the world, Captain Cook would meet his death on a trip ashore in Hawaii.

There was no lack of brave men eager to be a part of the voyage of exploration. Banks's own party finally included a naturalist named Spöring; another naturalist, named Solander, who had studied with the great Linnaeus; three artists to act as human cameras in a cameraless age; and four servants, two from the Revesby estate and two colored servants, probably Jamaican, who were to perish in the cold of Tierra del Fuego at the southernmost tip of South America. Of that party of ten, only Banks, Solander, and the two Revesby servants were to return alive after three years' absence from England.

Though they knew they were facing great risks, they were happy in their hopes of new discoveries when, during August 1768, the group of naturalists embarked on the *Endeavour* in Plymouth Harbor. John Ellis, another Fellow of the Royal Society, wrote to Linneaus of his adventurous colleagues: "No people ever went to sea better fitted out for the purpose of Natural History; they have all sorts of machines for catching and preserving insects; all kinds of nets, trawls, drags and hooks for coral fishing, they even have a curious contrivance of a telescope, by which, put into water, you can see the bottom

JOSEPH BANKS AND THE BREADFRUIT   19

at a great depth, where it is clear. They have many cases of bottles with ground stoppers of several sizes, to preserve animals in spirits. They have several sorts of salt to surround the seeds; and wax, both beeswax and that of Myrica; besides there are many people whose sole business it is to attend them for this very purpose. They have two painters and draughts-men, several volunteers who have a tolerable notion of Natural History; in short Solander assured me this expedition would cost Mr. Banks 10,000 pounds [more than $50,000 by today's standards]. All this is owing to you and your writings."

The *Endeavour* was a sturdy little vessel of sufficiently shal-low draft, it was hoped, that her bottom might escape damage on uncharted reefs and shoals. But a shallow draft vessel was bound to roll in any save the calmest seas, so that the hoped-for security must be paid for with almost constant seasickness of all on board. Three years of seasickness are an awful thing to contemplate. Worse, they did not purchase immunity from running aground.

Commissioned by the Admiralty to chart unknown seas once the astronomical observations had been completed, Cap-tain Cook proceeded from Tahiti to New Zealand, on which he, Banks, and Solander were the first Europeans ever to set foot. Then on to Australia, known as "New Holland," where the *Endeavour* scraped a nasty hole in her bottom on an un-charted reef. The hole was plugged with a sail, and all men on board, naturalists and astronomers included, manned the pumps while the ship moved cautiously northward to the near-est harbor equipped to repair damaged bottoms. Two months later they limped into Batavia (now Jakarta) in the Dutch East Indies (now Indonesia).

The skill and efficiency of Batavian shipyards delighted the seaman in Captain Cook, but as an officer responsible for the welfare of the men under him, he chafed at every moment of the three months required to repair the ship. Never a healthy spot, Batavia was worse than usual that year. One by one the ship's company, which had, through the Captain's skillful planning, escaped the usual curse of long voyages — scurvy — sickened of what now appears to have been malaria or dysentery or a particularly fearful combination of the two. Dysentery, bacterial or amoebic, was long to be a killer. Yet even then malaria could have been checked. But the "Peruvian bark" which might have provided effective control, though already known in Europe, was rejected by the smug, bloodletting physicians of that age.

So nearly half of the hundred men who had arrived in Batavia on board the *Endeavour* were buried either in the port or during the long voyage home. In August 1771 an unsigned letter was printed in a London newspaper. It described the whole situation, concluding: "Could we have proceeded by the Cape of Good Hope without touching there, I don't believe we should have buried above twelve people in this long voyage." A mere twelve casualties would have been something to boast about in the year 1771. This underlines the agonizing uncertainty of sea travel in the eighteenth century, when the eventual return of the ship itself from a three years' voyage was a matter for hope and prayer.

Though at the start Banks was scarcely more than a passenger on board the *Endeavour,* he soon moved into a position of some trust. The Captain, upon whose keen judgment of men so much always rested, promptly appraised young Banks's qualities of mind and spirit. Here was a man to be relied upon in a tight spot, a man who would not easily lose his head, a man with a trained observant eye and a receptive ear who could easily pick up bits of native languages and would deal strictly and fairly with the natives he encountered. Again and again the Captain would invite the young naturalist to accompany him ashore to help him dicker for supplies with the native tribesmen.

Of course a young man like Joseph Banks was exceptionally fortunate to be sailing in a ship commanded by so great a man as Captain Cook. Long after he had died, seamen found their proudest boast in the fact that they had sailed under him. To be a ship's officer under his command amounted to something like a postgraduate course in navigation and in that even more tricky science of commanding men.

Benjamin Franklin, minister plenipotentiary of the rebelling British colonies to the Court of France, paid willing homage to the great British captain. Immediately upon his appointment in 1779, he made haste to issue a "passport" for Captain Cook, then on his third voyage of discovery. Should the British ship and her captain fall into the hands of American armed vessels, Franklin instructed the officers of such ships: "You would not consider her an enemy, nor suffer any plunder to be made of the effects contained in her . . . but you would treat Captain Cook with all civility and kindness, affording them, as common friends of mankind, all the assistance in your power which they may happen to stand in need of." Though it would not be known for some months, Captain Cook was already beyond all human assistance on the shores of Hawaii.

Like Captain Cook, and possibly through his long association with the Captain, Banks developed a talent for winning the respect and confidence of all kinds of men. The Fellows of the Royal Society had already shown their regard. More significant, the men with whom he lived for so long at such close quarters on the *Endeavour* were still his friends after they returned to England. The natives of alien Tahiti remembered

him with affection and asked after him eagerly when Captain
Cook called there again during his second voyage. Back in
England, when young Banks was presented to his sovereign,
George III, he quickly won the royal confidence.

This last achievement was perhaps the most difficult of all
and would prove the most important to the science to which
Banks was dedicating his life. George III would seek his advice on matters botanical and horticultural, particularly in
connection with the Royal Botanic Gardens at Kew, whose
destiny the young naturalist would guide for many years. He
saw the gardens as more than a showy collection of beautiful,
interesting, and unusual plants, more even than an outstanding
accumulation of dried and pressed specimens from all parts
of the globe. In his vision, Kew Gardens was a center which
should send plant hunters forth into remote places to bring
back, sometimes at incredible risks, seeds and seedlings of new
plants. These should be planted in greenhouses or gardens at
Kew, tended and cared for there until they or their descendants
might be fit to set out again for the outposts of empire.

It was a dream worthy of an age when mariners like Captain
Cook were charting unknown seas. It is a dream that lives today when there are few seas left to chart. Throughout the
centuries it has sent men forth from comfort and security, not
the least of these being Sir Joseph Banks's friend and protégé,
William Bligh, captain of the ship *Bounty.*

When, in 1772, Captain Cook set out on his second voyage
of exploration, William Bligh sailed as ship's master mate. A
superb navigator like his captain, Bligh lacked the Captain's
genius for handling men. Unimaginative, touchy, quick-tem-
pered, Bligh was the kind of man to bring disaster both to
himself and to the men who were to sail under him. Yet his
equals, like Sir Joseph, thought well of him. Because of this

and because a man who had learned to know the South Seas under Captain Cook's guidance was needed, Sir Joseph used his influence to get Bligh appointed to the command of a ship whose trip to the South Seas Banks was busily sponsoring.

"I arrived yesterday from Jamaica," Bligh wrote Banks in August 1787. "I have heard the flattering news of your great goodness to me, intending to honour me with the command of the vessel you purpose to go to the South Seas."

Shortly thereafter Lord Sydney, who did not realize that this trip was Banks's own brain-child, wrote to Banks explaining the purpose of the expedition and asking for advice and help. "Dear Sir," the letter ran, "The Admiralty have, I understand, purchased a vessel for the purpose of conveying the bread-fruit tree and other useful productions from the South Sea Islands to His Majesty's West Indian Possessions. She is to be commissioned in a few days, to be called the *Bounty* and to be commanded by Lieutenant Bligh." Would Sir Joseph, he begged, prepare instructions for the gardeners whom the Admiralty would send along to secure and care for the plants during transportation?

The trees of Tahiti had already impressed both Joseph Banks and Captain Cook. "All these Islands," wrote the Captain, "are skirted round with a border of low land which is firtile and pleasant to a very high degree, being well clothed with Various sorts of fruit trees which nature hath planted here for the use of the happy natives. . . . These people may be said to be exempted from the curse of our forefathers. Scarce can it be said that they earn their bread with the sweat of their brows, benevolent nature hath not only provided them with the necessarys but many of the luxuries of life; Loaves of Bread, or at least what serves as a most excellent substitute, growes here in a manner spontaneously upon trees."

Bread on trees! And placed by provident nature in a part of the world where no grains grew! The crew and officers of the *Endeavour* had known the breadfruit well. They ate it gladly at the native banquets where they were frequently the honored guests. They remembered it and talked about it when they got home. "You won't believe it when I tell you — they treated us like kings — all of us including the commonest seaman — and they fed us bread that grew on trees." It was an incredible memory of an incredible trip that loomed more important with every passing year.

The breadfruit made a lasting impression upon Captain Bligh, too. "Inside it is soft and tender like the crumb of a penny loaf," he wrote enthusiastically. "There is neither seed nor stone inside but all is pure substance like bread."

It was the practical Joseph Banks who looked upon the breadfruit tree with a botanist's eye and who asked if there might be any good reason why the tree should not grow in other parts of the tropical world. Why not the British West Indies — Jamaica, say? What a boon it might prove to landowners and slaves alike! A cheap, satisfying substitute for the bread made from grains that did not grow well in tropical lands! Could seeds of the tree be expected to survive the long voyage in the moist heat of the tropics and in the icy cold of high latitudes? Probably not. But seedlings, carefully tended all the way . . . With care, surely, it could be accomplished . . . Something to think about, at least . . .

For sixteen years Joseph Banks thought about it, keeping the thought in the back of his mind. Sixteen years made the slight, eager youth into the rather heavy, imposing president of the Royal Society. His name had become one to conjure with in both social and scientific circles. He knew the people to talk to when he wanted to further his plans, and he knew how to talk to them. He talked frequently about the breadfruit and of what a boon it should prove to planters in Jamaica. In the end he achieved the commissioning of the *Bounty*.

Naturally, then, Banks had an answer ready even before he received Lord Sydney's letter: "The master and crew of the *Bounty* must not think it a grievance to give up the best accommodations. . . . The difficulty of carrying plants by sea is very great; a small sprinkling of sea water or of the salt dew which fills the air even in a moderate gale will inevitably destroy them if not immediately washed off with fresh water. It is necessary therefore that the cabin be appropriated to the sole purpose of making a kind of greenhouse, and the key of it given to the custody of the gardener and that in case of cold weather in going round the Cape a stove is provided by which it may be kept at a temperature of the inter-tropical countries. . . .

"As the plants will frequently want to be washed from the salt dampness, which the sea air will deposit upon them, besides allowance of water, a considerable provision must be made for that purpose; but as the vessel will have no cargo whatever but the plants on board, there will be abundant room for water casks, of which she must be supplied with as large a quantity as possible, that the gardener may never be refused the quantity of water he may have occasion to demand."

Clearly the pampered passengers of that voyage were to be the young breadfruit trees.

Captain Bligh had no slightest objection to the arrangement. His vanity was flattered that he had been chosen to command a ship which he would take along the route he had first traveled with the great Captain Cook. He was delighted to be collaborating with so grand a personage as Sir Joseph Banks,

President of the Royal Society, to whose views on matters horticultural even His Majesty was said to listen with respectful attention. Definitely, Captain Bligh congratulated himself, his fortunes were on the rise.

Had William Bligh been endowed with imaginative understanding of men, he might well have foreseen the possibility of trouble. They were a rough lot — the common seamen of his day — many of them forced against their wills into service by the notorious press gangs of the British ports who delivered crews to the ships at so much per head. In Tahiti these resentful sailors would find a delightful climate, charming companions, and a warm, generous hospitality which would build in them a conviction of their own worth. While the ship must linger in Tahiti to secure and load the breadfruit plants, the strict ship's discipline would be bound to weaken. Captain Cook would have foreseen this and forestalled it. Not Captain Bligh.

Even on the voyage out, the forecastle had been full of rebellious mutterings at the bad victuals, for which the Captain was blamed, and at his heavy-handed discipline. As soon as they set sail in Matavai Bay for the homeward voyage, this same heavy-handed discipline descended. The bullied men found it an unendurable aggravation to have to witness at the same time the tender care lavished on the silly green sprouts that filled every available nook and cranny of the never generous space on board a sailing vessel.

Not too many days out of Matavai Bay, mutiny flared up — one of the most famous mutinies of all time. The story of it is an oft-told tale. Captain Bligh and those officers and men who refused to join in the rebellion were put into an overloaded open boat and set adrift in the Pacific. Neither they nor the mutineers expected they could long survive. It was only slightly preferable to outright murder.

Alone of them all, Captain Bligh refused to give up hope. Here his bulldog determination and his unsurpassed qualities as sailor and navigator had full play. Determined to survive, to return to England, to have the mutineers hunted down and taken prisoners, Bligh bent every effort to bringing the boat and its heavy load of men through to safety. Still alive, if barely so, seventeen of the eighteen men who started out finally arrived in the harbor of Timor in the Dutch East Indies. David Nelson, botanist and plant hunter of the *Bounty* expedition, had died from exposure on the way.

Forty-seven days, thirty-six hundred miles, in an open boat, overloaded and with insufficient water supply! This exploit echoed round the earth to make Captain Bligh a hero and to win him the admiration and sympathy of all. The few mutineers who took up life on Tahiti were hunted down and brought back to England in chains to be tried and executed according to the laws of the sea.

Most of the mutineers, however, and the ship they had seized disappeared from the face of the earth. Despite vengeful search and unceasing inquiring in every port where ships of civilized nations might pause, for a long time no word of their fate drifted back to the land they once called home. Lost, perhaps, in a typhoon or a similarly violent storm, the Admiralty concluded. Then, many years later when the *Bounty* and her mutineers and her unusual cargo were all but forgotten, the children of those mutineers and the Tahitian women who accompanied them in their exile were discovered quite by accident.

When the heat of mutiny had cooled and the bullied and

humiliated men were able to think beyond the sufferings of the moment, they had to face the bleak knowledge that they had made themselves outcasts from all the civilized world. They dare not return home — they must not even appear in any known port. Mutiny was the blackest crime of the sea, a crime which no land with maritime interests could ignore. Even if Bligh and his boatload of men had disappeared, the *Bounty's* disappearance would also be known and every ship on the seas and every port be alerted. A single survivor would point to mutiny. No spot on the charts, however remote, could long protect mutineers from discovery and vengeance.

An uncharted refuge was the answer. Somewhere in the little traversed fastnesses of the Pacific, someone had once sighted a tiny island — or claimed he had. It wasn't on most charts. Many seamen didn't believe it really existed. But if it did exist, if the mutineers could rediscover it, it might be the sort of haven they needed. Luck was with them. They located the island — Pitcairn Island it is called today — unloaded the ship and sent it to the bottom where it could not betray the mutineers if a ship should wander off the usual routes of sailing vessels.

Thus ended the *Bounty* which was to have sailed triumphantly into a Jamaican harbor with a cargo of breadfruit trees. And thus began the mutineers' true punishment. Strife soon broke out among the bitter, rough, ignorant men who had condemned themselves to share this exile. Violence and death stalked into their midst. By the time Pitcairn Island was rediscovered there remained, out of all the original mutineers, only the gardener, William Brown, aging and chastened, to stand between the mutineers' children and complete savagery.

The innocent cause of all this trouble — the breadfruit trees — had followed Captain Bligh and the loyal men overboard, while the mutinying men jeered and laughed. Grown men to play nursemaid to a lot of silly plants you could get for the digging at Matavai Bay! Shade 'em from the heat of the sun, keep 'em warm when it turned cold, wash off the salt spray with drinking water! Who'd ever cared whether any seaman was hot or cold or sticky with salt! Let 'em try to wash the salt off those plants now! So ended one of the first recorded attempts to move useful plants from one land to another.

Back in England, though, neither the plants nor the mutineers were forgotten. No handful of mutinous seamen could turn Captain Bligh aside from his goal. Give him another chance, another ship, and he'd get breadfruit plants to Jamaica yet. Sir Joseph Banks, sympathetic and loyal towards the man whose unfortunate traits of character he had never personally experienced, saw to it that Captain Bligh had that other chance. In 1793, in command of the ship *Providence,* Bligh finally delivered a cargo of breadfruit plants to Jamaica.

"I give you joy of the success of your Plants," Bligh wrote Banks as his ship approached the island of St. Helena on the last lap of his voyage to Jamaica. "I am happily arrived with a beautiful collection in sight of this island. . . . I most sincerely pray you may live to hear they flourish and to know thousands are fed with their fruit."

News of the successful transplanting of the breadfruit seedlings traveled far and wide. Just one year later, George Washington wrote to Jamaica in hopes the Botanic Garden there might spare him some plants to try at Mount Vernon.

Thus, thanks largely to the efforts of Sir Joseph Banks, the whole world was becoming conscious of the uses of and need for plant exploration. In that age of expanding horizons, Sir Joseph was determined that his own science should not lag behind. He never let it be forgotten. Practically every successful botanical explorer of those days owed his inspiration to Sir Joseph. Frequently he owed much more.

The travel-experienced Banks had valuable advice to give to those who needed it. He also had influence with the Admiralty which he frequently used to find passage for hopeful explorers on ships sailing to remote lands. Quietly, neither asking nor desiring public acknowledgment, he would reach into his pockets and draw upon his personal fortune to help plant hunters less affluent than himself.

One condition only he made. The explorer should never forget the Royal Botanic Gardens at Kew. He should, whenever possible, bring home not only dried herbarium specimens but also living seeds and seedlings of exotic plants that might add interest or adornment to the greenhouses at Kew. Under Banks's guidance, the plantings at Kew Gardens increased by several thousand exotic plants and the fame of Kew Gardens spread around the world.

Some years after Sir Joseph's death in 1820, the Gardens he had so loved were saved from neglect and decay through the appointment of the botanist William Hooker to the directorship. Hooker had been the young man to whom, many years before, Banks wrote so disapprovingly when he let his family dissuade him from exploration in Java. William — later Sir William — was succeeded in 1865 by his son Joseph. Sir Joseph Hooker was a much traveled man in his own right who carried on the tradition of botanical exploration into our own century. Ever alert for useful crop plants, the Hookers arranged to have both quinine and rubber introduced into plantations of the expanding British Empire. As a partial consequence, the world which Sir Joseph Banks knew has changed almost beyond recognition.

III

Food for the Gods

WE ARE LEAST ABLE to trace the history of the plants we know best. Flowers and fruits and vegetables which our ancestors knew and used were commonplace long before the birth of modern systematic botany and before anyone thought to keep records of plant exploration. There might be many a fascinating adventure connected with the introduction of the African banana or of Ethiopian or Arabian coffee into large-scale cultivation, but we shall never know them in their entirety. We may guess that such introductions were accomplished by men who knew the products and recommended them to others, who may have passed on the plants to yet others, much as cuttings of house plants get passed on from one housewife to another. Thus, in general, it is of the important food plants that we have the least knowledge.

Breadfruit was one of the outstanding exceptions to this rule because breadfruit was unknown to any save the natives of a limited island area until an early voyage of exploration brought Europeans to the South Seas. Through their records, and perhaps because the *Bounty* mutiny was eighteenth-century front page news, we may follow the journey of breadfruit to Jamaican plantations. But in Jamaica we lose it. Today you may come upon breadfruit trees growing wild in many parts of lowland Central America but no one will be able to tell you their pedigree.

Another tropical crop that made a terrific impact upon the Europeans who first came to know it was cacao. Long before those Europeans got to America, it was a cultivated crop over large areas of the American tropics. From Mexico to northern Peru it was known and cherished. Where it was first discovered by the natives is not even a matter of legend. Nor have we a much better idea as to just how it made its way to other tropical lands. We do know that today it is grown in most fertile areas of the tropics.

It took a long time to get started, for the Spanish had no idea of permitting their American possessions to trade directly with one another, much less with outside lands. Spanish-American ports were supposed to be kept tightly closed to non-Spanish shipping. Only lawless men like buccaneers and smugglers would trade directly in contraband with the bolder and more independent Spanish-American settlers. Either these smugglers placed no value on chocolate or they could find no profitable market for it. At any rate, cacao remained almost a complete Spanish secret until the seventeenth century.

The Indians had always valued cacao. Montezuma, the Aztec ruler, had storehouses of cacao which he had received as taxes. Chocolate was his favorite drink and one he presented ceremonially to Cortez when he foolishly received the Spanish commander as an honored guest. The Spanish, who had come to conquer and rule, were promptly vanquished by the new delicious drink. It became an obsession of all classes. It even entered the *conventos* and became a wicked but almost irresistible temptation to the padres. For years it was a matter of heated controversy.

If you are one of those people who have, at some time, sworn off chocolate for the duration of Lent, you undoubtedly did so as you might have other sweets. Surely you never thought of chocolate as a dangerous temptation of the devil, an inflamer of passions, a drink which the truly godly must try to avoid. Yet in the sixteenth and seventeenth centuries that was the considered opinion of many wise and holy men. But not of all.

In remote, lonely conventos scattered in tiny Indian settlements among the mountains and valleys of Mexico and Guatemala, these padres uncomplainingly endured many hardships as they sought to save the Indians' souls by converting them to the Christian faith. Mastering the strange, guttural Indian tongues was only one of the hardships. Clad in coarse, heavy habits, sometimes completely barefoot, often shod only in open sandals, they trod the hot, dry, dusty trails from village to village. Water was often scarce. The sun's rays beat upon them cruelly. Often they must rest themselves on burning sands, in the doubtful shade of a bullthorn acacia or of a spiny cactus. The one compensation the unkind and alien land might grant them would be a calabash full of delicious chocolate at the journey's end.

Cacao was an ever present problem to all conventos. Fray Remesal, who kept a careful account of life in the conventos of Guatemala and Chiapas, now a part of southern Mexico, mentions it again and again. He tells how his Order received instructions to sell all its farm lands so that the padres might not be faced with the distractions farming afforded. Soon, however, they had to repossess the lands which they then planted to sugar cane and cacao — which, obviously, they planned to use as needed.

Rules of management and behavior were discussed freely in meetings of the Chapter. The padres accepted these strict rules without too much complaint. Only one they found too stringent: that no one under sixty years of age be permitted to drink chocolate. Whether these older ones were supposed to need the nourishment chocolate might supply, whether their age put them beyond danger, or whether their years of devoted service won them this special indulgence, Fray Remesal does not say. He does say, though, that this rule forbidding chocolate to the younger ones, only made them crave the drink more.

Another account of those years tells of the novices in the Santa Clara convento, whose imposing structure still stands, only partially destroyed by the eighteenth-century earthquakes that leveled to the ground so many of the beautiful churches of Antigua Guatemala. Beneath the church was a crypt where dignitaries of the Order were buried. To the novices this seemed a quiet, remote place where they might safely indulge

in forbidden cups of chocolate. In the midst of one such feast they were confronted by the master of novices rising specter-like from behind a tomb. They scattered in guilty terror.

Other accounts of chocolate come from an English Dominican friar by the name of Thomas Gage who served and traveled extensively in New Spain (Mexico). He gives elaborate recipes for the preparation of a variety of chocolate drinks, which included everything from pepper to cloves. A hearty man, he consumed great quantities of chocolate without — so he assures us — ever suffering any ill effects. A calabashful upon rising, another between nine and ten o'clock in the morning, another following midday dinner, another between four and five in the afternoon, and, if he sat up late, yet another before retiring — such was his daily routine for twelve years.

Gage was well able to sympathize with folk who loved their chocolate. Yet even he thought the people of Chiapas carried it a bit far. Ladies of Chiapas found it impossible to sit through church services without having their maids bring them chocolate to drink. The good bishop in the cathedral there was frankly shocked to find not only sermons but Mass — even High Mass — interrupted by the entry of these maids bearing foaming calabashes. On the cathedral door he posted his interdiction threatening excommunication to anyone who disobeyed him. The ladies paid no attention, so the bishop ordered assisting priests to take the chocolate from the maids as they attempted to enter. A general fight broke out and thereafter the ladies forsook the cathedral for cloister churches whose monks and nuns forbore to interfere with their customs.

Presently the bishop died under circumstances that led his physicians to suspect poisoning. The finger of guilt seemed to suggest one of the infuriated chocolate-drinking ladies as the poisoner. Friar Gage, who had previously been glad to accept gifts of chocolate from her, thought better of receiving such gifts in the future.

Samples of cacao beans had gone back to Spain with Columbus and failed to convince the stingy queen, Isabel la Catolica, that the Admiral's discoveries could compensate for the East Indies to which he had promised to find a short, direct route. Like most people, she thought only in terms of familiar products of known value. Though in 1528 Cortez already had introduced into Spain the hot, vanilla-flavored drink, it was nearly another fifty years before it really caught on there.

France first heard of the drink in 1600 or thereabouts. Probably long before, French monks had introduced it into French monasteries. The drink did not become fashionable in that land, though, until the Spanish princess, Maria Teresa, married Louis XIV of France in 1660, bringing to Paris her Spanish retainers and their Spanish customs. In 1657 the first chocolate house in England advertised in the *Public Adviser:* "In Bishopsgate Street, in Queen's Head Alley, at a Frenchman's House, is an excellent West India drink called Chocolate to be sold, where you may have it ready at any time, and also unmade at reasonable rates."

"Reasonable rates" meant perhaps from two to three dollars a pound by modern reckoning. Naturally addiction to such an exclusive and costly drink served to underline a man's refined and elegant taste. Chocolate houses grew to be highly fashionable. Cacao had arrived as a product much in demand. The rejected bean was already outdistancing many of the products Queen Isabel had coveted.

The year 1765 saw the first chocolate mill of North America opened in Dorchester, Massachusetts. By 1790 the annual import of cacao beans into the United States was a half million pounds; by 1900 it had reached 20 million; by 1950, 700 million — the estimated yield of 1.4 million acres of cultivated cacao.

Like the scrub apple trees of New England hillsides — trees whose ancestry no one can trace — cacao trees spring up wild throughout tropical America. You may come upon one almost anywhere there in the very heart of the jungle. Its foliage is varicolored according to the age of the leaves — from pinkish brown through dark green to a mottled yellow for the oldest leaves that hang limply on the boughs or litter the ground beneath. The almost black surface of trunk and main branches is studded with surprisingly dainty pink blossoms on very short stems, or with the maturing fruit that may be as large as a cantaloupe and colored in almost any tint between yellow and purple. The trees grow well in conveniently placed clearings where men, having harvested the fruit of other trees, have cut out the beans in their pulp and accidentally dropped some into the black, fertile soil. Nobody either knows or cares when or how.

Linnaeus, who must have heard many of the legends surrounding this tree, named it *Theobroma cacao. Theobroma* — "food for the gods" — is an appropriate name. But it is the fact that for many centuries it has been a cherished food for men that has made its ancestry and its travels so difficult to trace. The plants that are easiest to trace are those whose importance men were slow to recognize.

IV

The Fever Bark Tree

WHEN, IN 1803, Thomas Jefferson negotiated his Louisiana Purchase, political enemies pointed out that the President was throwing the citizens' money away on a dismal swamp unfit for human habitation. Even several decades later, a traveler would write back from Illinois: "But, of all other epidemics, the 'fever and ague' is the scourge of the West. . . . When severe and protracted, it completely shatters the constitution;

and the victim ever after bears about him a living death." In many areas, this fever and ague caused settlers to abandon fertile lands and leave behind all their investments of time and money, to return to poorer though healthier homes.

It was no new illness, this, nor was it in any way peculiar to the New World. It was actually as old as recorded history, and in the days when the sad lines quoted above were written the remedy was already at hand for those who would reach out and seize it. In Arrow Rock, Missouri, Dr. John Sappington was dispensing his Fever Pills, for which he claimed no personal genius of discovery, to the brave or desperate souls who were ready to try them. The active component of these pills was no secret, their effectiveness was dramatic, yet two centuries after the drug had first been brought to the attention of European physicians, it was being given only the most grudging recognition.

And thereby hangs a tale.

The tropical lands of the Far East have produced many things, material and cultural, which we of the West have come to value. Yet we might never have known many of those things had not another continent produced a drug which could control the fatal misery of the ancient shaking fevers. Alexander the Great, young and triumphant world conqueror of the fourth century before Christ, was finally vanquished in India by this fever. He died shaking as miserably as the least of his soldiers. For centuries few of the Europeans who visited the wonderful lands of the Orient lived to return and tell of the people and their legends. In Batavia, remember, all but one of the company of the *Endeavour* sickened in the course of a three months' stay.

In earlier centuries men called this shaking fever "ague." Today we call it "malaria." We recognize the malarial parasite when we meet it on a microscope slide. We know the kind of mosquitoes that carry it from man to man and we know how they carry it. We know the type of place where such mosquitoes breed and how to prevent this breeding. Yet we would still be helpless against the disease they carry had not our conservative ancestors finally brought themselves to try a remedy sponsored by some untutored Indians in a remote corner of Spain's colonial empire.

The physicians of those early days were not interested in Indian remedies. Nothing of value, they knew, could come from heathen who had mastered none of the wisdom of ancient physicians like Hippocrates, who lived about four hundred years before Christ, or Galen, who lived about a hundred and fifty years after Christ. Nevertheless, the bleak fact remained that all the wisdom of these ancients had not helped to abate by one tiny bit the sufferings of people whom the ague held in its deathly grip.

It was the missionaries in Spanish Colonial America, Catholic padres who lived close to the people in the remoter portions of the Spanish realm, who observed the astonishing fact that there might be some better method of treating the ague than by bleeding the sufferers white in the hallowed names of Hippocrates and Galen. Today we know that by itself, without bloodletting, the malarial parasite brings about a serious anemia. Perhaps those early physicians did shorten their patients' sufferings — though hardly in the way they claimed to.

"A tree grows which they call 'the fever tree' in the vicinity of Loxa," wrote the Augustinian monk, Father Calancha, about 1633, "whose bark, of the color of cinnamon, made into powder of the weight of two small silver coins and given as a beverage, cures the fevers and tertians; it has produced miraculous results in Lima."

Yet even though some striking cures were ascribed to the fever tree, most people in Lima rejected it. They had, perhaps, to prove their sophistication by refusing to take seriously a native remedy for a disease that had baffled for many centuries the wisest and most skilled physicians of Europe.

"My dear!" we can almost hear a once lovely lady of the vice-regal court exclaim in a period between her typically intermittent seizures of fever. "Fancy using a remedy from one of those heathen witch doctors! Ridiculous! Now my doctor — Juan de Vega, you know — is personal physician to His Excellency, the Viceroy, and I count myself lucky to be one of his patients . . ."

If the fever bark found a cool reception in Lima, it encountered positive hostility in Europe. Doctors might change their ways slightly with the passing years, but it would not be by adopting a remedy sponsored by nonmedical missionaries in a distant and barbaric land. The only way the fever bark could gain acceptance must be through the agency of men outside the medical profession.

In justice to the physicians of the seventeenth century, it is only fair to admit that not even all the Indians native to the Viceroyalty of Peru were familiar with the virtues of the fever bark. More than two centuries after Father Calancha first wrote of the fever bark tree, Indians living not far from Loxa would refuse medication with that bark. And when they saw men from other lands determined to collect and carry off seeds of the fever bark tree, they would exclaim in disbelief, "A cure for fever, Señores! Ah, no! It must be that you hope to use this bark to prepare a valuable dye for your ponchos and will not share the secret with us . . ."

Of course, if there was any secret concerning the fever bark tree — which we now call *Cinchona* — it had long been the special property of those Indians residing near Loxa, or of some other Indians who had originally instructed the inhabitants of Loxa, who thought enough of Father Calancha to share their secret with him. But how the wonderful properties of the cinchona were first discovered, who really discovered them, and how the rather difficult question of proper dosage was settled — why the secret was at first so carefully guarded and then so reluctantly shared — there is not even the shred of an ancient native legend to tell us. Perhaps some of the wise physicians of the highly cultured Inca Empire discovered the drug and guarded it for the use of the great nobles of the Inca Empire — but perhaps anything. As the Spanish say, *quién sabe* — who knows?

The great and noble Count of Chinchon, the Viceroy of Peru whose name the fever bark tree now bears, was the first man to try to introduce the fever bark tree into Europe. But when, by these efforts, he brought upon himself only the fury of the doctors, he desisted. No coward, he believed that well-trained physicians certainly must understand more about such matters than a mere government official could hope to.

The next man to sponsor the bark in Europe was himself learned enough to realize that even learned specialists could not know everything — and perhaps, too, humble enough to understand that the most unlettered men can know much. Juan, Cardinal de Lugo, a Jesuit padre of great wisdom and energy, devoted so many years to promoting the bark that it came also to be known as "The Cardinal's Bark" or "The Jesuit's Bark." Yet, despite its high-placed and noble-minded sponsors, the fever bark was almost universally rejected. All over Europe, men who should have been desperate enough to give any remedy a try continued to shake with the ague, be bled white by their physicians, and to die long before their time.

What nobleman and churchman had failed to accomplish was finally achieved by an English practitioner whom all the medical profession agreed in denouncing as a quack. Consider, now, the incredible nerve of the man, who refused to bleed his patients, who dosed them with neither violent purges nor emetics, but simply saw to it that they partook regularly of his "secret" remedy. If those patients had died under his care, physicians would gladly have brought the quack to swift justice as a murderer. They found it still more unforgivable that his patients appeared to recover.

Least forgivable of all, perhaps, was that the quack, Robert Talbor by name, numbered among his patients many members of the reigning houses of Europe, including Charles II of England. By way of reward the quack was finally knighted, and died in 1682 as Sir Robert Talbor, with only a very few people having guessed the secret of his remedy. And this may have been just as well in times when to dose an English monarch, head of the Church of England, with a bark sponsored by a Jesuit cardinal could easily be called treason. Had Charles II died from any cause whatsoever during the course of Talbor's treatments, death would surely have come to Robert Talbor, promptly and in one of those especially horrible forms reserved for traitors. Fortunately for himself, Sir Robert, the quack, was a man of courage and imagination — and luck. Fortunately for us, he confided his secret to someone else, to whom he also gave permission to reveal it after Sir Robert's death. So the curative properties of the bark, having received royal approval, could no longer be rejected.

The queen of Charles II was a Portuguese princess whose dowry brought to the English the right to trade in the Portuguese settlements along the coast of India — a privilege of little value as long as traders there were almost certain to sicken and die of the ague. The fever bark tree and the quinine eventually prepared from it in pure crystalline form were to make it possible for Europeans not only to trade safely in India, but also to make their homes there as well. In the end the fever bark brought relief to thousands of the East Indians themselves.

The fever bark tree! Where exactly did it grow? What did it look like? How was it to be distinguished from trees of other families? Some barks yielded a lot of quinine, others very little. How might these barks be assayed so that the dosage of patients need not always have to be determined by the tedious and sometimes risky method of trial and error? Or was this talk of bark only a means of concealing the real source of the powerful medicine? When you really investigated the subject, you'd find that not even the missionaries who proclaimed the bark's wonderful powers had set eyes upon a living fever bark tree.

No longer ridiculing or rejecting the idea that a worthwhile drug might come from the bark of a South American tree, men began to want to know more about that tree. It was time for botanists and plant hunters to take a hand. Yet botany was such an infant science and South America so remote and unvisited — partly because Spain had kept the ports of its overseas possessions carefully closed to foreigners — that it took a long time to bring this about.

Somehow, in 1735, permission was granted for a group of French scientists to visit South America so that they might measure the length of the earth's meridian at the equator near Quito in what is now Ecuador. The three principal members of the group were, of course, primarily geographers, though no scientist of that century learned enough to be a member of the French Academy would dream of confining his interests to one narrow field. Attached to the expedition in a minor capacity was a man, Joseph Jussieu, whose main interest was botany.

Though they originally planned to remain in South America no more than three years, seven had passed before the first member of the group returned to France. Thirty-six years later, the last member — Joseph Jussieu — would arrive in France a raving lunatic. Compared with the elaborate expeditions of today, it was a strangely disorganized affair. Before their time was up, various members had to sell personal belongings to help finance their stay. They got into controversies with the natives. As a result, the expedition's surgeon was killed. While the natives, both Spanish and Indian, watched with disdain, expedition members disagreed violently and the expedition split up.

Though, to judge by their bickerings, they would not have been above deserting one another, the botanist, at least, remained in South America because he wanted to. Joseph Jussieu decided that before returning home he would make a complete study of the fever bark tree. It was an ambitious scheme whose difficulties he could not possibly foresee. He intended to view these trees in the remote mountain fastnesses where they grew, make careful records of their variants, test their barks for potency, leave absolutely nothing in doubt. It would be the botanical masterpiece of the century — win him, without a doubt, membership in the great French Academy.

Since he knew no one whom he might interest in helping finance the undertaking, he financed it himself. He earned money as he needed it by teaching botany, practicing medicine or engineering, designing bridges, dams and roads and supervising their construction. The years went by and he grew from youth to middle age and beyond. Yet he never forgot the main purpose of his stay in South America. Every bit of information he could accumulate upon the fever bark tree he stored away in great boxes that accompanied him wherever he might go.

Joseph Jussieu's native servant often looked at those boxes and asked himself what kind of treasure the strange master might be carrying within. But the master foolishly kept them locked, forgetting that none but he could care a bit about the manuscripts and maps and dried plant specimens they contained. Had the servant seen them, he would have thought his master mad. Not ever being permitted a glance inside, the servant concluded his master was rich. Someday, he dreamed, the master would grow careless and he would be able to help himself. Then, one day, he realized Jussieu was preparing to leave for his far distant home, taking the treasure chests with him.

The servant could not bear the thought of losing the riches he had so long promised himself. He swiftly made off with the precious boxes into the trackless jungle. When, at a safe distance, he opened them and saw the dry plants and brittle papers, he must have felt bitterly deceived. Probably he cursed his cheated master. For he certainly could not have seen in the disappointing contents of those boxes twenty-five irre-placeable years of another man's life — years which had made him sick and old and given him nothing save the dreams which alone make a lonely life endurable.

With those papers, Jussieu lost everything that had given his life meaning. For ten years he disappeared from sight and no one ever knew whither he had gone or what he was doing all that time. We can imagine him hopefully, agonizingly, following one dimming jungle trail after another, always seem-ing to be on the point of catching up with the faithless servant and with the papers which, long before the years were up, must have rotted away.

In 1771, Joseph Jussieu arrived back in France so completely deranged that no one was ever able to get from him an account of those lost ten years. Nor was anyone ever the wiser for his long, painstaking, tragically futile years of study of the fever bark tree. Only from another member of the original expedition — from one who had no pretensions to botanical eminence — Charles Marie de la Condamine, was to come a brief description of the tree which would enable the great Linnaeus to give it a place in botanical classification.

In 1761, the same year that the no longer young Jussieu was making ready to transport his precious boxes back to France, an enthusiastic young man came out from Spain to the "New Kingdom of Granada" — today the Republic of Colombia — full of his own dreams of botanical exploration. The youth, José Celestino Mutis, was a medical school graduate yet without interest in the practice of medicine unless it could bring him closer to the realization of his dreams. An able doctor with unlimited opportunities for a remunerative practice, he chose the unprofitable study of plants.

From Cadiz, the Spanish port where José Mutis grew up, great galleons were constantly setting out for the fabulous New World. The boys of the town sat on the quays and watched these ships come and go, kept their eyes open for the cargoes that were unloaded, and their ears to the sailors' conversations from which they picked up bits of information about the lands beyond the wide sea. Many a boy must, like Mutis, have dreamed of the day he himself might set forth in one of those ships. But few dreamed strongly enough to try to bring their dreams to fulfillment.

As he grew to manhood, Mutis realized that he must have

money or influence or both if he wished to reach American shores. Since he had no personal fortune and no friends with money or influence enough to set him up as a botanist in Spain's overseas possessions, he accepted a post as personal physician to the Viceroy of the New Kingdom of Granada. The Viceroy wanted a personal physician enough to assure the reluctant youth that he would be allowed plenty of leisure to pursue his botanical studies. Once in the viceregal seat of Santa Fé de Bogotá, the Viceroy promptly forgot his promises.

The Viceroy, who knew well enough that residence in Bogotá involved risks to his health, had no slightest idea of letting his personal physician wander far afield on trips of botanical exploration. So he saw to it that the foolish though able young doctor was kept busy in the capital with a rapidly expanding medical practice. To another physician the wealthy and fashionable clientele of the viceregal court might have been all that a medical heart could desire. Not so, however, to the youth who wanted only to write an exhaustive and immortal, if unprofitable, treatise on the plants of the New World.

He was in a most difficult position. To resign his post would leave him without any means of support. To continue in it must prevent him from doing the work he had dedicated himself to. In 1763 he tried to solve this problem by petitioning the king, Charles III of Spain, for support of his projected study.

"America," Mutis wrote in his petition, "is not only rich in gold, silver, precious stones and other treasures, but also in natural products of the greatest value. . . . There is quinine, a priceless possession of which Your Majesty is the only owner and which divine Providence has bestowed upon you for the good of mankind. It is indispensable to study the cinchona tree so that only the best kind will be sold to the public at the lowest cost."

To sell the best quinine at the lowest price to a general public could not seem very important to a king at a time when only the boldest of his subjects could dream of questioning the divine right of kings to rule and, hence, do as they might wish to. Perhaps the King found a disquieting hint of republicanism in Mutis' further suggestion that if he failed to finance a study of quinine, he might later be haunted by the shades of those who died of fever when, by royal foresight, they might easily have been saved. Plebeian shades haunt a king, indeed! Naturally Mutis received no royal help.

Perhaps if Charles III of Spain could have foreseen that an ever increasing demand for fever bark would presently strip the Spanish dominions of their most accessible supplies and of the income they brought, he might not have turned so deaf an ear to Mutis' petition. Mutis wanted more than just a systematic study of cinchona. Once the study had been made, the best varieties determined, he wished to use the information for the purpose of starting cinchona plantations. Self-interest might have moved the king where interest in the people's welfare failed, had he known that the production of fever bark was to pass out of Spanish hands.

Meanwhile José Mutis kept doggedly on, taking every moment he could spare from his practice to seek for the cinchona tree where it had never previously been reported — in the vicinity of Bogotá. To find it would be more than a mere botanical truimph. If New Granada produced the tree, then the bark could be shipped direct to Europe from its Caribbean ports instead of having to make the long Pacific voyage north from Peru to Panama, to be transhipped by mule train across the Isthmus and then loaded again on ships on the Atlantic side.

Able to stand it no longer, Mutis fled from his medical practice to live and study botany in a remote silver-mining community. There he was located in 1782 by a new viceroy, a churchman and scholar, Archbishop Antonio Caballero y Góngora. Able to recognize the exceptional talents of the now fifty years old Mutis, Caballero persuaded him to return to Bogotá by assuring him he need not again undertake medical practice. The Archbishop further used his influence to induce the King to pay Mutis' debts, purchase for him whatever books and instruments he might need, grant him a salary, and even to finance an expedition for the purpose of studying the cinchona tree in its native haunts. It seemed that at last Mutis was to realize the dreams of his youth.

In the recently founded Botanical Institute of New Granada, Mutis could pursue his studies without interruption or distraction. Many young men came to work there and receive instruction from him. The central point of all this work was the fever bark tree. The quantity and complexity of the information assembled, the numbers of carefully drawn and hand-colored plates, and the unceasing study should have made the work the masterpiece of Mutis' youthful dreams. But Mutis, the perfectionist, never could quite bring himself to call the work finished. Always there was some more important information to be collected, another plate to be drawn to make the manuscript ready for publication. Mutis finally grew blind and ill while the work was unfinished. In 1808 he died, leaving the completion of his life's work to one of his devoted students, Francisco José de Caldas.

By 1808 Spain's American colonies were seething with

unrest. One by one they revolted and broke away from the mother country. Leading and encouraging these revolts were students and scientists. And in the forefront of these, sad to relate, was Francisco de Caldas. So when, during 1816, the Spanish imperial forces temporarily gained the upper hand in New Granada, Caldas was seized and executed as a traitor.

With Caldas' death ended all hope of finishing the work on the fever bark tree as Mutis had wished it to be done. Knowing this, Caldas had begged his captors for a few months' reprieve. He would work with chains about his ankles, he protested, just so that the work on cinchona might be brought to completion. The Spanish commander refused. Perhaps he was an ignorant man who could see no possible use in science. Certainly he must have realized that time was on the rebels' side and a delayed execution would turn out to be no execution at all. Very soon all Spanish forces had to leave New Granada for good. Before leaving, they packed up all the contents of the Botanical Institute — instruments, drawings, papers, maps — and shipped them back to Spain where, for many decades, the boxes remained undisturbed and unopened under thickening coats of dust.

Many men had dedicated their lives to the study of the cinchona tree, yet nearly two hundred years after fever bark had been introduced into Europe, the natural history of the tree which produced it was still unknown and physicians still were inclined to regard the bark as of, at best, highly questionable value.

At this point the young science of chemistry took a hand. In 1820 two French chemists, Caventou and Pelletier by name, managed to isolate from cinchona bark two powerful alkaloids — "quinine" and "cinchonine," they called them — which could be shown to be the active principles of the bark. It would be many decades later that other chemists would look inside the molecules of these alkaloids and learn just how the individual atoms of carbon and hydrogen and oxygen were linked together to produce such powerfully active drugs. Still more decades would pass before such molecules could be put together in the laboratory. Yet they never have learned — and probably never will — to rival the efficiency and economy of the living laboratory in the long-despised fever bark tree.

Perhaps you may be inclined to think that the preparation of a pure crystalline compound would make the drug more acceptable to reluctant physicians. Surely a nice white pill should have more medical appeal than a powder of dirty bark. Unfortunately, the doctors had already passed final judgment upon the bark and any products derived therefrom — or thought they had. So most of them continued to dose their patients with powerful emetics, to purge them and to bleed them and, in the name of their medicine, to kill them with kindly ministrations.

Fortunately there were a few less conservative men who were willing to grant that the new crystalline drug might have something of value. They could now use it on patients who had found that the dark powder disagreed with their digestion. Moreover, by swallowing pills these patients might avoid the extremely bitter taste which they had found so revolting in the powder. Best of all, the pills permitted a carefully regulated dosage for the control of the fever.

So wrote Dr. John Sappington of Missouri in his book, *The Theory and Treatment of Fevers*, published by him in 1844 after a long and successful practice in the treatment of fevers. "The names of Caventou and Pelletier," he wrote, further, "who first separated the pure alkaline salt, called *quina*, from the bulky and inert mass in which nature had placed it, de-

THE FEVER BARK TREE 53

serve to be remembered with gratitude by all mankind.

"Since that fortunate era in medicine, I have been enabled to administer the bark at any stage and in any quantities that I might think advisable. . . . The discovery has not only afforded me heartfelt gratification, — for the reason that it enabled me to give more prompt and certain relief to the sick, — but it has been instrumental in giving me a character and standing in my profession, well calculated to excite the envy of the physicians around me. But this I desired not; for I did not conceal from them, in our consultations, my views on either the theory or practice which gave me such superior success. It seemed that the most melancholy experience was not sufficient to convince them of their errors, and they still, from the mere force of education, considered my practice as empirical."

If the shade of Sir Robert Talbor ever wandered far enough from his lifetime haunts to reach the western banks of the Mississippi, it must have smiled in sympathy and amusement to see Dr. John Sappington selling his remedy as "Sappington's Anti-Fever Pills" and — to use the doctor's own words — "concealing their composition that they might acquire a reputation upon their own intrinsic worth."

In any case, quinine and the tree that produced it could not much longer remain ignored. In 1849, four years after the publication of Dr. Sappington's book, a French botanist named Weddell finally produced the much needed systematic study of *Cinchona,* of which, by then, many species were known. From his jungle travels, Weddell brought back seeds of the cinchona tree, so that they might be planted in greenhouses of England and France and, at long last, give the people of those lands a chance to become familiar with the long-ignored tree.

The time for starting plantations was definitely at hand. As the drug acquired medical respectability and more and more doctors prescribed it, the uncertain supply and high cost of wild cinchona caused increasing alarm. And whose the responsibility to face this need? Not Spain's, for she no longer wielded power in those lands where the fever tree grew wild. The new young American republics were too preoccupied with other matters and too conscious of their individual rivalries to co-operate in preserving their priceless natural resources. So it became the concern of foreigners — of the British who needed to control the fevers of India, and of the Dutch who had the same kind of needs in Java. Besides, cinchona might prove a profitable crop plant for those tropical lands.

In all this, no one consulted the Indians of the Andean highlands where cinchona grew. The lands and all the fruits thereof had always belonged to their ancestors and, as far as they were concerned, now belonged to them. The Spanish were nothing more than annoying interlopers. Dead cinchona bark might be sold for profit. All the *cascarilleros* — bark gatherers — were Indians and knew the market value of this product. Being shrewd and intelligent, they also knew what might happen to this market if they sold either trees or the seed which produced them.

In the Amazon basin, the botanist Richard Spruce was discovering that suspicious Indians might steal seeds he had collected, boil them, then put them back. He could not know for many months that his collections were valueless. In the Bolivian highlands where the best cinchona grew, Indians were even more determined to hold inviolate what they knew to be their own.

Few civilized men know enough to take seriously the unlettered savage's unwillingness to part with his possessions. A shinier mirror, these strangers think, a brighter length of trade goods, and the bargain will be closed. This was the belief of Justus Karl Hasskarl, Director of the Botanical Gardens in Java where he hoped to start cinchona plantations. When, both in Bolivia and in adjoining Peru, he found his hopes frustrated, he made connections with a shady local character named Henríquez, who agreed to deliver the desired plants for a large sum of money.

Henríquez kept his part of the bargain and, in 1854, delivered to Hasskarl the required number of cinchona seedlings. Hasskarl paid him off and set out promptly for Java with the precious plants. It was really none of his business that the natives of the regions whence Henríquez had stolen the plants threatened to cut the thief's feet off if ever they could get their hands on him. With enough money to live on quite comfortably, Henríquez kept well away from the jungles. In the end the Dutchman held the bag. He had paid for inferior and sickly plants which could bring nothing of value to his Gardens in Java.

The British were the next to try their luck in the high rainforest where cinchona grew. And they, too, might have had no better luck than Hasskarl, had it not been for the dedicated English scientist and plant hunter, Richard Spruce.

Born in Yorkshire in 1817, Spruce had always dreamed of becoming a plant explorer. In 1849, without any financial backing, he set out for the jungles of the Amazon and adjoining Rio Negro. Joseph Banks had been dead twenty years and there was no one else who could or would take his place in the financing of botanical exploration. Banks would have admired his young countryman's enthusiasm and self-dedication and would have encouraged and sponsored his work of exploration. But in 1849 all he could contribute to Richard

Spruce was the tradition of botanical exploration he had always done everything in his power to further. William Hooker, then director of Kew Gardens, had no great private fortune or, apparently, the power to persuade men of fortune to contribute generously to the expenses of expeditions like Spruce's.

Today, when we read so many accounts of elaborately planned and financed and equipped expeditions, it is hard to imagine how a poor young Englishman could have had the courage to undertake such a trip without any visible means of support save the hoped-for income from plant specimens. He planned to collect, dry, and press many duplicates of the new and interesting plants he must encounter in so unexplored a region as he planned to penetrate. These specimens he would ship back, as opportunity afforded, to friends in England who had agreed to arrange for their sale and send the proceeds to the plant hunter in South America, so that he might be able to collect more for them to sell.

That an adequate income might be expected from such an arrangement seems hardly possible to us. Yet even today it might be done, for good plant collections have a real if limited market value. And in the time of Richard Spruce there were, throughout Europe and America, plenty of private herbaria and public museums that wished to acquire representative collections from remote lands and would pay for these collections at so much per specimen. This uncertain and irregular income, plus the few months' government pay he drew while collecting cinchona seedlings, was all Spruce had to live upon during the fifteen years he spent in South America. He had even less when, his health broken, he returned to his native land.

For eight years, mostly alone with native guides and servants, Richard Spruce penetrated areas of the Amazon basin where no man of science had ever before set foot. His observant naturalist's eye, quick to spy out interesting plants, was equally alert to the whole scene about him. In his carefully kept journal, as in his plant collection, he lives again today.

He moved along the Amazon and its tributaries from one small primitive settlement to another. Sometimes he had to cope with violent storms and raging floods. At other times — many times — he found his native help incompetent. Yet only once did he record any serious personal trouble with those poor, remote natives who well might have been tempted to slaughter this Englishman, alone in their midst, for the small articles of civilized manufacture and the trade goods he carried with him. Most of the Indians liked and trusted the odd foreigner who was not above enjoying himself at their festivals and who really tried to talk to them in their own tongues.

If any foreigner could succeed in the ticklish business of getting seeds and seedlings of the cinchona out of the jungles which the Indians regarded as their own, it would be Richard Spruce. So, at least, reasoned the director of Kew Gardens, who may not have understood too well the difference between the natives of the Amazon lowlands and the Indians of upland Bolivia and Ecuador where the desired red cinchona grew. Even these Indians could see immediately that Spruce was no sly, cheating Henríquez — that he could do his own plant exploring and collecting — and that he would be unlikely to find their most remote and valuable stands of cinchona.

In any case, whatever the Indians of upland Ecuador may have thought of Spruce, they did not pursue him with active violence. Perhaps they expected their ancestral gods to assume responsibility for his punishment. And, in a way, they were right. For Richard Spruce, his health already undermined by eight years in the steaming lowland jungles, endured sheer misery in the penetrating damp cold of those high slopes of the extinct volcano, Chimborazo, where the red cinchona grew. His health never quite recovered from the effects of his residence there.

Though he was assigned two Englishmen — one a resident of Ecuador and the other a gardener from Kew — to aid him, the ultimate responsibility was Spruce's. The first problem was to locate an area where fine red cinchona could be secured. This turned out to be in the vicinity of a place named Limón where "existed formerly the finest manchon of Red Bark ever seen. It was all cut down many years ago, but I was informed that shoots from the old roots had already grown to be stout little trees large enough to bear flowers and fruit." The tragic end of a crop which destroyed the tree that bore it was becoming all too evident. Plantations were being planned none too soon.

Spruce and Dr. Taylor, the Englishman residing in Ecuador, next had to approach the men who had title to this land where the desired cinchona grew. "With these two gentlemen," Spruce wrote in his report, "I had, therefore, to treat for permission to take from the bark woods the seeds and plants I wanted. At first they were unwilling to grant me it at any price, but, after a good deal of parley, I succeeded in making a treaty with them whereby, on the payment of 400 dollars, I was allowed to take as many seeds and plants as I liked, so long as I did not touch the bark."

Labor, which the Ecuadorian gentlemen agreed to help him secure, was largely made up of half-breed squatters on the land. The gentlemen's help proved to be of doubtful value, for the whole land was in a state of civil war and any able-bodied man might be conscripted by one side or the other, depending upon which spied him first. Worse still, light-fingered soldiery was constantly passing and repassing the Englishmen's camp. Small articles were constantly disappearing. Pack mules which Spruce had gathered for the purpose of transporting cinchona seedlings to the coast, were also conscripted. The outlook for cinchona plantations in India seemed as cold and depressing as the forests around Limón.

Somehow, Spruce managed to collect the seedlings and get them transported to a little river port called Aguacatal, and then transhipped to a raft he had had constructed for the purpose of carrying them further to the ocean port of Guayaquil. "Some difficulty," Spruce wrote in his report, "had been experienced in procuring the requisite number of beasts of burden, and the making of cylindrical baskets to contain the plants had proved a tedious task; besides that, the tying up each plant in wet moss, and the packing them in the baskets, were delicate operations which Mr. Cross [the gardener] could trust to no hands but his own. There had been not a few falls on the way, and some of the baskets had got partially crushed by the wilfulness of the bulls in running through the bush; but the greater part of the plants turned out wonderfully fresh. . . . As we might expect some rough treatment on the descent to Guayaquil, we did not put on the glasses, but in their stead stretched moistened strips of calico over the cases, which seemed to answer admirably." At the river port, the plants had already been transferred to wooden cases filled with a mixture of "earth, sand, and dead leaves" in preparation for the long voyage across the ocean. It was these they covered with calico.

The raft trip held its own dangers for both plants and men. "The river had risen to its winter level and . . . is narrowed in some places to 30 yards, and the navigable channel is fur-

ther straitened by the trees which hang far over the water.
Add to this that the river ran like a sluice, and that the turns
were frequent and abrupt, and it will be seen how difficult it
was to maintain our clumsy craft always in the mid-stream.
. . . At length at a sharp turn, the raft went dead on, and
through a mass of branches and twiners that hung over the
middle of the river. The effect was tremendous: the heavy
cases were hoisted up and dashed against each other, the roof
of our cabin smashed in, and the old pilot was for some moments so completely involved in the branches and the wreck
of the roof, that I expected nothing but that he had been
carried away; he held on, however, and at last emerged, pant-
ing and perspiring, but with no further injury than a smart
flogging from the twigs, which indeed none of us entirely
escaped. . . .

"Our deck now presented a lamentable sight, but we had
little time for ascertaining the amount of damage, as at every
turn a similar peril awaited us." Thus ran the three days' river
journey which brought them to Guayaquil. "The plants,
thanks to Mr. Cross' tender care of them, bore scarcely any
traces of the rough treatment they had undergone in their
descent from Limón and in their late voyage from Aguacatal,
and the only thing against them was that they were growing too
rapidly, owing to the increased temperature to which they had
lately been subjected."

Two days later Richard Spruce saw his plants stowed aboard
a freighter. "[I] then took leave of Mr. Cross and the plants,
satisfied that as long as they were under his care they were
likely to go on prosperously, and having done all I could on
my part to conduct the enterprise to a successful issue." Successful it definitely was. In 1860 cinchona plantations were

finally started in India, in Ceylon and, through a gift of young trees to the Dutch government, in Java. And Richard Spruce, briefly financed plant hunter, went back to his self-supported plant collecting.

"Cinchona succirubra," he recorded in his journal, "is a very handsome tree and, in looking over the forest, I could never see any other tree at all comparable to it for beauty."

Beautiful though it looked to Spruce, who had been specifically directed by his government to collect it, its content of that all-important alkaloid, quinine, turned out to be less than hoped for. In the end it was not a botanist but a trader, Charles Ledger, who would secure viable seeds of the best cinchona species, eventually to be known, in his honor, as *Cinchona ledgeriana.* Yet Ledger himself would have been the first to say that he secured those seeds at too high a price.

Charles Ledger went out to South America in 1836 with the hope of making money by purchasing there and reselling at home articles in high demand — alpaca wool, for instance, and cinchona bark. Because he was a kind man, of wisdom and integrity, his affairs prospered. He won the respect of the Indians, who are not easily impressed by outsiders and who are quick to see the flaws beneath a civilized veneer. No Henríquez could fool them as he did Hasskarl. So it is testimony to Ledger's high qualities of character that the Indians who knew him well were devoted to him.

Ledger made his home in the town of Puno on the Peruvian end of the high, bleak Lake Titicaca. Upon this huge lake, and upon the incongruous little steamer that now makes regular trips between the Bolivian end and Puno, the snow-clad peaks of the Andes look down with cool, distant aloofness. The Indians who make their homes along the rush-lined shores of the lake care very little just where the line runs that divides Bolivia from Peru. As far as they are concerned, the land is all theirs.

Of these Indians, those called Aymaras are the most fanatically devoted to their land and to its fruits. It is said they would sooner sell their children than part with their ancestral acres. Always reserved, they might serve foreign masters for money, yet never give them their first loyalty. Personal devotion to a foreigner like Charles Ledger could only bring tragedy to an Aymara, for it involved a conflict of deep-rooted loyalties. So it proved with Ledger's servant Manuel, who had lived long in his house and grown to love him.

Manuel's people could find nothing objectionable in Manuel's serving the outsider, nor even in his helping Ledger obtain highest-yielding barks. But when Ledger tried to find where these fine barks grew, tried to secure seeds and seedlings of the trees which produced them, Manuel knew well enough he must make a bitter choice: the master whom he had served for eighteen years, whose fortune he had helped make, who trusted him in everything, or his own people and their inviolable traditions. Either he must lead his master to the desired cinchona trees or he must leave him.

So, after eighteen years of living in the foreigner's house, he returned to his own people to take up work as an independent cascarillero in their cinchona forests. Now more a stranger to his own people than to Ledger, he still yearned for the good man — still wished to prove his undying devotion. Four years later he returned alone across eight hundred miles of bleak Andean highlands where travelers resting by the wayside might freeze into seated statues. Concealed in his long hair, Manuel brought a packet of seeds for the man he loved. They came, Manuel said, from an especially fine stand of cinchona trees he had encountered in the course of his bark collecting. Then he took his departure to return across the frozen miles to his people, who he knew would regard him as a traitor should they ever learn of his act.

The betrayal, as Manuel had expected all along, was discovered and punished. Years later, Manuel's son, who also had lived long in Ledger's house, told of his father's death as a traitor. Then the youth offered to collect more seeds for the Englishman, should he still wish them. Touched by this devotion, horrified to learn what it had brought to the youth's father, Ledger promptly rejected the offer.

Actually, it was no longer a matter of such great importance. For the tragic collection of cinchona seeds — in which, surprisingly, it now seemed difficult to interest the British government — was finally sold, half to a British planter in India and half to the Dutch government. Today the best plantations of Ceylon and Java — which turned out to have climates better adapted than India's to the growing of cinchona — are covered with descendants of the trees which sprouted from seeds paid for with Manuel's life.

What of quinine today? Still a treatment for malaria and still best derived from the ancient fever bark, it is no longer — save as plantation sources may be cut off by wars — sought by cascarilleros along the high Andean slopes which look at the snows. Now tamed, the most beautiful tree of the forest grows in orderly rows where men have placed it until such a time as other men choose to slaughter it by stripping off its bark.

Plantation life, however, has brought the tree new problems undreamed of by the early plant hunters. When a tree moves from its nearly solitary state of scattered small groups among an almost infinite number of other trees into organized communities, it must also face the risks of community living. Insects which like to feast upon it settle happily near such plantations to grow fat and multiply. Infections, no longer quarantined by natural isolation, spread easily from tree to tree.

Resistance to disease does not seem to go hand in hand with high yields of quinine. Where the plant hunter left off, the plant pathologist and the plant breeder soon had to take up. Today they graft high-bearing trunks upon disease-resistant roots from lower-yielding varieties. The result is something less pretty than the tree Richard Spruce described so enthusiastically. But who cares? The cinchona is still the most beautiful tree in the forest to millions who, but for it, might have sickened and died of that ancient disease, the shaking fever.

V

Kalaws and Kings

FREED FROM THE WORST EFFECTS of malaria, Englishmen finally began to settle and make their homes in India. They learned its language, came to know its people, heard its legends. Presently they began to hear rumors that some of the natives of that land knew how to cure the ancient disfiguring disease, leprosy. The cure was said to depend upon an oil produced by the "kalaw" tree.

Leprosy first made its appearance in Europe during the eleventh century when Crusaders brought it back with them from the Near East. People infected with the disease frequently came to look so horrible that, through the centuries, the word "leper" took on the meaning of "outcast." Then, eight hundred years after the Crusades, men of the West began to ask, at first incredulously, then with increasing hope, if they might not find a cure for the disease in the jungles of the Far East.

Once upon a time — so ran the Indian legend which the at first rather contemptuous Englishmen heard — there lived in Benares a king named Rana. Neither his power nor his wealth could protect King Rana from infection with leprosy. Perhaps, one day, he discovered under his skin the small lumps that, to those familiar with the disease, suggest the onset of leprosy. Perhaps he pressed them and found that he could feel nothing and then, in panic, tried cutting himself there with the tip of his sword and still found he could feel no pain. He knew the worst.

For a while Rana could conceal the lesions from others if not from himself. But eventually the ravages of the disease could not be hidden from those about him. The nodules increased in number and became open sores which would not heal even under the care of the most dedicated of court physicians. Flesh and the tissues underneath began to wear away and would not be replaced. In dread he saw himself becoming noseless, faceless, fingerless like other lepers.

Soon his courtiers guessed the worst and began to find excuses for leaving the court. No royal favors, no lavish gifts, could repay them for running the danger of contracting the dread disease. Seeing this and knowing that his son, too, might become infected if he remained in Benares, Rana finally abdicated his throne in his son's favor and went forth into the jungle, there to live far from his fellow men.

The hollow in a great tree became the king's only shelter. His diet was made up of roots and herbs and, particularly, of the fruit of a tree the natives knew by the name of "kalaw." Presently, to his delight and astonishment, Rana found that his disease was leaving him and soon he knew himself to be entirely cured, feeling better than he had while living amid the luxuries of his palace in Benares.

In a cave not far from the hollow tree lived the once beautiful Piya, princess of a neighboring kingdom. Deserted in the jungle by brothers and sisters who had discovered she was a leper, she, like Rana, had had to fend for herself. She, too, managed to keep alive on roots and herbs, though somehow she overlooked the wonderful kalaw.

One day a tiger stalked Piya into the cave which was her home. When she turned and saw the terrible beast making ready to spring upon her and tear her apart, she screamed so loudly that Rana, who happened to be passing nearby, was attracted to the hidden cave mouth. Naturally he rescued the princess from her frightening danger. And also naturally, he rescued her from the ravages of leprosy by teaching her to eat of the kalaw. Piya soon became once more her own fair self and the dazzled ex-king married her. They lived happily ever after in the jungle kingdom they shared, raising sixteen pairs of twin sons which, in due time, Piya bore her lord.

A charming legend! Yet could it, by any chance, be more than a legend, more than a fantastic fairy tale? Could it contain some germ of truth? Had Rana and Piya really lived, really been lepers, really experienced a seemingly miraculous cure? Or had someone less exalted experienced a cure and used that cure to weave a romantic tale? Was there really a kalaw tree and, if so, what manner of tree might it be? Oil reputed to be from this tree could be bought in the bazaars of Calcutta. Cures seemed to have been effected by it.

Was there something, then, to that rancid, ill-smelling, and dirty "chaulmoogra" oil that was sold at so high a price in the markets of India? No matter how fantastic the claims might sound, doctors could not afford to ignore any possible means of curing the previously incurable. If there were even a slight hope that the seeds of this kalaw might offer help to sufferers from leprosy — now called "Hansen's disease" — they must be investigated. The legend must be checked in the laboratory.

Seeds must be secured. Carefully controlled tests must be made. For this alone all the oil then available in the markets of India probably would not suffice. And just in case the oil turned out to be as represented, plantations must be started. It would not do to wait idle during the years in which data were being accumulated. For it would take another eight years at least to grow trees of sufficient size to bear fruit and produce the oil. You did not save money or effort in a matter in which people's lives might be at stake.

What to do, then? Buy seeds, plant them, tend the young plants — and, lo, you have a plantation! A wonderfully simple idea, but it had one important flaw. In the 1840's, when it was first proposed, people in Indian cities had not the slightest idea as to what kind of tree the kalaw might be. If dealers in the bazaars offered you seeds which they claimed to be of the kalaw, you had to believe them, for you had no alternative. Yet those seeds had been picked off the ground in the jungles of northeastern India or Assam or Burma or, even, Siam. You could have only the assurances of the illiterate tribesmen who collected the seeds that they really came from the trees you sought. A useless vial of chaulmoogra oil need not be too serious, for the next would probably be satisfactory. But where you are undertaking an eight years' commitment, it's well to be absolutely sure all the time.

People had to learn the hard way that in every region of the general area there was a different tree that the natives called "kalaw."

"What's in a name?" mourned Juliet. "That which we call a rose, by any other name would smell as sweet."

Yes — if, indeed, it is a rose. But suppose you did not know what a rose should smell like? Suppose someone offered you an ill-smelling plant like a skunk cabbage as a rose, would the name by itself be sufficient to make it smell sweet? Before you agreed it was a rose, you'd have to know just what was meant by "rose" — what special plant characters go to make a rose a rose and how, through them, you may always with reasonable certainty determine a rose.

You are, of course, privileged to call any person or any plant by any name of your own choosing. But if you wish to discuss the subject intelligibly with other people, you'd better be sure all of you know just what you're talking about. You cannot afford to talk a private and secret botanical language of your own invention, particularly if the plant in question may be as important in the lives of as many people as, eventually, the kalaw tree proved to be.

"Kalaw" was not, of course, the kind of name botanists would assign, but it was the only one, for quite some time, they had to go by. A botanical name should place a plant in a family with its close relatives. It is a two-part affair, the first part being a genus name, the second that which concedes the plant to be a distinct species in the general genus. So it was with *Cinchona succirubra* and *Cinchona ledgeriana* — both belonging to the genus *Cinchona,* yet each a distinct species of that genus. So it would have to be eventually with the kalaw when it might be identified botanically. Some folk think it very funny that grown men should devote any time trying to call plants by their right names. Plants couldn't care less, they say. But, as in the case of the kalaw tree, humanity can care a great deal.

To start the first plantations, kalaw seeds were purchased in the Calcutta bazaars. This seed was carefully planted, the shoots carefully tended until, years later, they grew into trees large enough to bear fruit. When the fruit was collected, the seeds removed, the oil pressed out, it seemed that the goal was near. Now men had a controlled, fresh supply of kalaw seeds. Large-scale treatments and tests might be begun. No one expected miraculous or even immediate results. A slow-developing disease could not be cleared up in days or weeks.

Yet as months and years went by without any conspicuous improvement, ever skeptical physicians began to pooh-pooh that so-called wonderful native cure. Witches' tales — nothing more — just what you might expect. . . . Others would not give up so easily. Perhaps some loophole might have been left. Perhaps plantation-grown trees did not have the vigor to produce curative oils; perhaps there was something hurtful in the soils where they grew; perhaps the oil had not been properly expressed. It might also be that the patients selected for the test treatments had more deep-seated infections. On the other hand, the skeptics might be right. All those reputed cures of the past might not be cures of genuine Hansen's disease but of some skin infections that, superficially at least, resembled leprosy.

Whatever the cause of failure might be, the oil began to fall into disrepute among Western physicians. As it eventually turned out, the real trouble was in the name. The kalaw they had wasted so much time and effort and money upon was the wrong tree.

Only some fifty years later was the actual source of chaulmoogra oil botanically identified. In the year 1890, Colonel Prain, then director of a botanical survey in India, wrote enthusiastically to one of his colleagues, "Your 14421 from Chittagong is a great find. These are the real chaulmoogra seeds of the Calcutta bazaars and of the Paris and London drug dealers." At long last the kalaw tree, the special one desired, had been tracked to one of its lairs, Chittagong.

Nevertheless the discouragement caused by the failure of the first kalaw plantations long persisted. About twenty years later another man — a plant hunter by profession — could still write of the kalaw tree: "Dealers in chaulmoogra oil have never seen the tree in its wild state. Even the native Bengal dealers in Chittagong had not been in the forests of the Chittagong Hill tracts. All depend on jungle people . . . who are more or less indolent. Moreover . . . at least 50% of the crop is lost every year. The Burmese name kalaw is applied to more than one species, and these species resemble one another so closely that the jungle people make no distinction between them. . . . [These trees] do not bear a regular crop but . . . sometimes are without fruit for two years or more. The natives stated that the fruit is collected by them every three years.

"The remoteness from civilized centers of the forests where these trees occur, the dangers and difficulty encountered in collecting the seeds . . . point to the necessity of starting plantations of *Taraktogenos kurzii,* which is known to yield true chaulmoogra oil, and also of such species . . . as yield oils of similar composition. . . . It has been stated . . .

that owing to the very encouraging work carried out in Hawaii and the great success achieved in the treatment of leprosy with chaulmoogra oil derivatives, the lowest yearly demand will be for 1,000,000 litres [264,170 gallons] of oil. . . . With this in view, the expedition was undertaken . . . for the purpose of securing viable seeds of as many species as possible."

The man who wrote those lines — Joseph F. C. Rock — was extraordinarily well fitted to undertake such an expedition. Born in Vienna, Austria, in 1884, he early developed an absorbing interest in botany and a talent for mastering foreign languages, including the very difficult Chinese. In 1907 he received an appointment to teach in the University of Hawaii, where he gave instruction both in the Chinese language and in botany. Up to 1920, when he resigned his university post, Rock made a botanical name for himself through his unusually fine collections of Hawaiian plants. In later years he would make similarly fine collections in China and Tibet. Herbarium specimens labeled "Collector: Joseph F. C. Rock" may today be found in most herbaria where plants from the Pacific area are preserved.

A naturalized American citizen in 1913, Rock joined the Plant Introduction Service of the United States Department of Agriculture in 1920. This Service was then becoming increasingly conscious of the desirability of searching previously unexplored areas of the world for new plants that might be grown in American flower or vegetable gardens or in orchards. Joseph Rock, botanist and linguist combined, was just the kind of man the Service needed.

A rapid traveler who could take care of himself in out-of-the-way spots, he had a determination to let no obstacles come between him and whatever plants he set out to secure. Definitely, he was the man to track *Taraktogenos kurzii* to its native haunts. Since the medical value of chaulmoogra oil had already been demonstrated, the plant hunter was in pursuit of something more substantial than a legend. Yet as the plant he sought continued to elude him again and again, he must have begun to wonder about its reality. Characteristically, Rock traveled light and moved swiftly, either unaccompanied or with native companions. Tedious and difficult though his journey must often have seemed to him at the time, the names of the places through which he passed read — to our Western ears, at least — like the stuff of which real legends are made.

Disembarking from his steamer at the port of Singapore, Joseph Rock first faced a rail journey of 1018 miles to Bangkok, Siam — now Thailand. A thousand-mile rail journey does not today sound like adventure. Yet a slow train that ran sluggishly through lowland tropical jungles each day and stopped each night at some small settlement is somewhat different from our accepted idea of rail travel. Each night the passengers found what accommodation they could in crowded, hot, comfortless, not always clean rest houses. Six days and five nights of this could easily constitute adventure.

Bangkok seemed no bit nearer the object of the plant hunter's quest. He could find no one there who had any idea as to where the kalaw tree might be found. So he traveled on, asking questions of everyone he encountered, getting nowhere fast. Finally, in the upcountry town of Chiengmai, the Viceroy's wife recalled that she had heard people say the tree was plentiful near her girlhood home in Korat. To Korat, Joseph Rock set out at once. Yes, the people there agreed, the tree did grow in the nearby jungles. Just where? That would be hard to say. A tree that made such excellent firewood was usually cut down before it got very big. Sometimes it was very hard to find. And as for any trees growing big enough and mature enough to bear seeds — now that was hardly to be expected.

Back in Chiengmai in early December and still empty-handed, the plant hunter chartered a houseboat for a ten days' journey down the Meh Ping river to Raheng. The starlit nights were cold with a heavy soaking dew that might become a heavy shroud of fog by morning. When, as day progressed, the fog lifted off the surface of the water, he could feast his eyes upon extraordinarily beautiful scenery — narrow, steep-walled gorges, perhaps, or the gentler distant hills forested with mighty bamboos and silk cotton trees. In the space of those ten days, the houseboat had to negotiate forty-one rapids. Though during the nights they remained moored and fog-bound, they found these had their own terrors. An elephant herd might go rampaging through a clump of bamboos, eating the smaller canes, trampling upon the larger ones, and crushing the hollow sections with a noise as deafening as machine gun fire and perhaps, coming as it did through the stillness of the jungle night, even more terrifying.

Raheng, the end of that journey, still produced no kalaw trees. So Joseph Rock decided to head across the forested mountain ranges to Moulmein. Amid these giant trees, some of which soared to more than 150 feet, he encountered a few kalaw trees, but these bore no fruit and hence, from his point of view, were valueless. Each night the little party camped in the jungle. The jungle animals —leopards, tigers, snakes — left him undisturbed. Christmas Eve found him in Moulmein, where he took a day off in the company of missionaries resident there.

The day following Christmas, Joseph Rock set off once more, this time for the Martaban Hills of Burma. With him went an interpreter, a cook, and a houseboy — though there was to be no house. In fact, they actively avoided houses and the villages where swarming ticks and mangy dogs made the less certain menace of attack by wild animals in jungle camps a highly preferable risk. In the Martaban Hills, Rock actually encountered a single kalaw tree in fruit and carefully collected the precious seeds — 170 in all — to send home to the Department of Agriculture. So many miles, so much hardship, so many dangers, for a few seeds that might never sprout!

"Much of the seed is lost," wrote the collector from America, "as the native collectors do not take the fruits from the trees when ripe, but wait until they drop, a much less troublesome way to collect them. However monkeys are fond of the fruit flesh and attack the fruits on the trees, dropping the seeds to the ground: and many of the seeds are lost in the crevices between the innumerable rocks and boulders. Porcupines also devour the seeds and the result is that in all probability about 50 percent of the crop is lost."

But men were still the tree's worst enemy, cutting it for firewood or destroying it in a more long-drawn-out manner by gradually removing the bark. The natives considered that a tea brewed from this bark would serve to treat intestinal disorders and skin diseases. Living kalaw trees were marked by tying strings around the trunks. Then, as the medicine might be needed, they would send children to the jungle to cut enough bark for the doses they thought they should have. Soon large areas of bark would be removed from these living medicine chests. Even if the now defenseless jungle giants were not killed by girdling, white ants and termites would get to work and speedily bring them low.

The 170 seeds from a single tree were in no way sufficient. So Joseph Rock, listening to rumors that he might find trees in the upper Chindwin district of Burma, set out again, his destination Rangoon.

Though by now it seemed that the kalaw trees must always be where he was not, Rock could not afford to overlook any lead. Arrived in Rangoon, he took the train through a semi-desert region to "dirty, dirty Monya" on the upper Chindwin River.

The dust in Monya was several feet thick. In this dust mangy dogs fought noisily. Squatting women chewed constantly on betel nuts and spat as constantly into the dust. Piles of rotting fruits and vegetables added the final revolting touch. Without a shade of regret, the explorer set forth from Monya the next day on the stern-wheeler *Shillong,* bound for Mawlaik.

By eleven o'clock, when they were happily clear of the town, the fog lifted to reveal a pleasing view of boats in midstream and people in colorful costumes along the banks. At Mawlaik, Joseph Rock paused briefly, not to collect kalaw seeds, for he knew the trees to be still several days' journey beyond, but to secure a letter of introduction, written in Burmese by a local government official.

This, which he called his "magic letter," turned out to be of tremendous value. If he just showed it to the headman of a town, there would be conjured up almost at once all the coolies he needed to carry his baggage out and his collections back. Of course there was the consideration of two cents per mile per man, but money without the magic letter was powerless to secure coolies. The first part of the journey was by dugout canoe. This was followed by a two days' march afoot, in the course of which the river was crossed and recrossed times without number. Finally they arrived at their destination, a town bearing the outlandish name of Khoung Kyew.

Here, at last, Rock came upon his first genuine chaulmoogra

tree, the earlier ones having been only closely related species which also produced curative oils. Here was the long-sought-for *Taraktogenos kurzii*. It would have been too much to expect a good crop of seeds in the first village visited. But at last weary of eluding the pursuer — or so it seemed — a good stand of the trees bearing mature fruit and seeds was encountered in the next village. There, too, was another collector of seeds — a she-bear with her cub. When the natives raised a loud shout, she fled, leaving both seeds and cub behind.

Finally loaded down with seeds, they started back to the village along the path they had taken on the way out. Fresh tiger tracks brought to them the chilling realization that they, too, had been hunted. Perhaps the shouts had frightened off the tiger as well as the bear. Or perhaps the tiger decided that the departing bear might make easier and tastier game. Perhaps it was the same tiger that later that night attacked one of the nearby villages, killing three women and a little girl as they huddled helpless in their flimsy shelters.

While coolies and villagers spent the next night in an organized tiger hunt, the plant collectors delayed their departure. A fearful storm came up, lightning flashed almost continuously. Frightened by the storm, a herd of elephants went rampaging through the town, trampling huts, ruining the crops in the fields, devouring stored grain, bellowing noisily all the while. The tiger was caught and killed but the whole village was ruined.

With this dramatic climax, the long quest was ended. There were enough seeds in the collections to start plantations in various places — in greenhouses in Washington, outside in Hawaii and the Philippines. Enough had also been learned about the growing habits of the trees to make these plantations successful. The trees would in due time mature and produce seeds of their own from which oil might be prepared or new plantations started. The cycle of planting and growing and harvesting was on its way.

The time would come soon enough when, convinced of the effectiveness of chaulmoogra oil, chemists would study the secrets of its molecules and would learn how to change them slightly, by adding this or that small chemical group, to increase the oil's effectiveness in vanquishing disease. They would even learn to draw a diagram of the atoms in each molecule of chaulmoogra oil and, final chemical triumph, manage to synthesize some of these molecules. But they would never learn — nor really hope to do so — how to achieve all this as cheaply and as effectively as the plants.

Those seeds were far more than small brown lumps that, with luck and care, would eventually produce tall trees. They were months out of a plant hunter's life, lonely weeks along jungle-bordered rivers and wilderness trails, fogbound mornings and starlit nights, quaint villages, colorful villagers, wild bears, stalking tigers, and rampaging elephants.

Most of all, they were an ancient legend realized. Rana and Piya almost live again in the curative powers of chaulmoogra oil. Yet not quite — for it is impossible to eat the products of the kalaw tree without becoming violently nauseated. Even the flesh of animals and fish that have eaten fallen seeds seems almost inedible. Today this fact doesn't matter, for a derivative of the oil is now injected directly into the patient's veins. Today's patient is spared the nausea. It's hard to believe that King Rana, ignorant of the kalaw's curative powers, could ever have eaten enough to make the discovery. But then it's hard to believe anyone could; yet someone did, and that someone surely merited a crown.

VI

The Weeping Tree

IT WAS ALMOST EXACTLY like any other jungle clearing in low-land Central America, the casual observer would have said. But a botanist, spying the tall alien tree that grew there, could not have agreed. That tree, like the lilies and lilacs of the deserted New England homestead, had a tale to tell. Though the accident which had placed it there was either unknown or long since forgotten, its presence marked the clearing in a very

special way. Even the plantation help, to whom one great tree
was pretty much like another, could perceive that this particular tree must be different.

Each morning as the swift tropic dawn swept darkness from
the sky, they would look through the doorways of their houses
towards the edge of the encroaching jungle and watch the
plantation manager, accompanied by his houseboy, come into
the clearing and scan the ground under the big tree. Every ripe
fruit, every scattered seed was gathered up. Soon, the plantation knew only too well, the seeds would be planted in a
nearby seedbed and the young shoots would be carefully
tended and moved on into larger plantations as soon as they
attained sufficient size to fight their own battles for survival.

The plantation workers had no way of knowing how important this survival might be to the world in general. That
their manager put a great store in it, they knew. It just didn't
make sense, they told one another with shaking heads and
smiles that suggested the boss was going off his rocker like
many another man who had come to tropical America from
northern homes. At one moment the manager nagged them to
cut down every single plant shoot that might dare show itself
within the circle of the clearing. Then he would turn right
around and make a fuss about collecting seeds and growing
seedlings from another tree neither more handsome nor more
useful than the ones he was always having cut down.

They knew, of course, that if they scratched the bark of the
tree, milky tears would ooze out and run briefly down the
bark until it congealed into a rubbery clot. They'd seen milky
juice before. It could mean very little to them that this tree
bore the scientific name *Hevea brasiliensis* or that it could
trace its proud ancestry back through rubber plantations of
the East Indies and exotic plantings in the greenhouses of Kew

Gardens to the tablelands above the Rio Tapajos in Brazil. Nor could they know that by then, in the nineteen-twenties, both Brazil and the Indies had become so covetous of the seeds, so determined to protect their own traffic in the magic white juice, that new plantations could be started in other lands only from such seeds as they watched their plantation manager gather in his strange daily ritual.

More than four centuries had passed since Columbus, visiting Haiti on his second voyage of discovery, saw natives playing with balls that bounced. In 1521 another Italian, named Pietro d'Anghicra, wrote of balls "which being stricken upon the ground but softly . . . would rebound incredibly in the aire." Of course practically everything connected with this New World seemed incredible to men of the Old. If the first explorers tried to investigate more closely and to find out of what those balls were composed, they made no record of the attempt. Nor did they bring samples of such balls back with them to a Europe as fascinated by the New World as we of today are by outer space.

A century later, another returning traveler recorded that the bouncing balls "were made from the gum of a tree grown in the hot country, which having holes made in it, distills great white drops that soon harden, and being worked and molded together turn black as pitch." The blackness probably was due to the heavy smoke of the oily palm nut fires which were used to smoke the gum in the process of hardening and molding.

It still remained a curiosity of the New World, months away across stormy seas, and no one in Europe could dream of any future or fortunes in bouncing balls or in the strange material of which they were made. What was needed then, as now, was perceptive, unbiased eyes with which to examine previously despised primitive products. Needed, too, were an imagination not schooled to set ways and the kind of resourcefulness possessed by the pioneering spirits who were then treading the new pathways of science.

It was more than mere accident that made the French geographer and mathematician Charles Marie de la Condamine, in 1735, the first to grasp the uniquely valuable possibilities of products made from the gum of the "weeping tree." French Academician and director of the expedition of which the tragic Joseph Jussieu had been a member, La Condamine dabbled in all sciences, including botany, as was the fashion for scientists of that age. It was La Condamine who succeeded in bringing specimens of the fever bark tree back to France. La Condamine also took notes on caoutchouc — soon to be called "rubber" — on its sources and its methods of preparation. He sent home articles manufactured of this rubber and thus awakened in Europe the first really active and general interest in the product. By the time Joseph Banks visited Lisbon in 1766, caoutchouc was a much talked about novelty.

"The rosin named 'Cabout-chou' in those countries of the province of Quito . . ." wrote La Condamine, "is also very common on the banks of the Marañon, and serves for the same uses. When it is fresh, they work it with molds into what shape they please, and it is impenetrable to the rain, but what renders it most remarkable is its elasticity. They make bottles thereof which it is not easy to break; boots and hollow bowls which may be squeez'd flat, and when no longer under restraint, recover their first form."

La Condamine then went on to describe the syringes — really squirt guns — which the Omagua Indians made from this same gun and used playfully upon one another. Each guest at an Indian feast would be supplied with such a syringe. "The use of the squirt," he noted, "with them is always a prelude to their most solemn feasts."

Flexible, unbreakable, elastic, waterproof, easily molded to whatever form might be desired — what a combination of rare and useful properties! Just the thing, the geographer perceived, to make cases for delicate surveying instruments which corroded so easily in the damp tropical heat. So La Condamine had rubber cases made for his instruments and with that the gum of the wild tropical tree really emerged from the jungle.

The name "rubber" was to be born in 1770. "I have seen," wrote Joseph Priestley — Dissenting minister, enthusiastic scientist, discoverer of oxygen — during that year, "a substance excellently adapted to wiping from paper the mark of a black lead pencil. It is sold by Mr. Navine, the instrument maker." So the new substance which would presently find a thousand more important uses received its name because it came from the Indies and it might be used for rubbing out pencil marks. India rubber!

For decades after Joseph Priestley had given it its name, rubber would remain a rare and curious substance. Rubber had a serious drawback which other natural products, like quinine and chaulmoogra oil, did not. These latter could be prepared from the plants which formed them at any distance from the source of supply and at practically any time, no matter how long, after the plant material was harvested. Since the juice of the rubber tree promptly coagulated in the air, articles manufactured of rubber had to be molded in the jungles where the trees grew. Until men could devise some means of softening the already coagulated rubber and then remolding it, the variety and uses of rubber articles must remain limited.

In North America and in England, men were working hard at the problem. By 1813 a gentleman of Philadelphia claimed invention of a "varnish" which might be used to rubber-coat and hence waterproof shoes. Here was born the idea of using a volatile solvent — something that would dissolve rubber and then evaporate when it was no longer needed. A year or so later, an Englishman named Hancock patented a means of manufacturing crude rubber gloves, tobacco pouches, elastic garters, and — most wonderful of all — waterproof cloaks for the use of stagecoach passengers. If they were expected to be used only by coach passengers, these cloaks must have weighed a great deal. Even so, they must have come as a blessing to men who knew the miseries of riding outside in thick fogs and driving rains.

Meanwhile South American trade was expanding as the growing merchant fleets of Massachusetts sailed into the mouth of the Amazon and dropped anchor in Belém de Pará. There adventurous and resourceful Yankees encountered the Amazonian Indians and saw the waterproof boots made by these Indians by coagulating successive layers of rubber latex over their own crude hand-carved wooden lasts. Waterproof boots! Certainly the answer to a sailor's prayer! What a comfort such boots might prove both in tropical downpours and in cold North Atlantic storms. The Yankee seaman purchased some for his own use. The Yankee trader — usually the same person — stocked some boots to try on the home market.

One Captain Benjamin Upton, Salem tradition runs, in 1824, was the first to introduce Brazilian "gum" shoes into

Salem. They proved quite as useful in Salem's snowy, slushy streets as in the mud of Pará, so they caught on fast. Customs records of Pará show that in the period between 1836 and 1842, three quarters of a million pairs of such shoes were shipped to Salem, Massachusetts. This was almost as many pairs as had been purchased by all the rest of the world put together.

Yankee ingenuity had combined with Yankee adventurousness to achieve this result. For it soon developed that the gum boots had serious drawbacks. Proportioned to fit the bare feet of a race much smaller in stature and frame than the North American sailors, the first pairs proved none too comfortable for their purchasers to wear. To remedy that, Salem shipmasters secured shoe lasts from nearby Lynn, already a center of shoemaking, and carried them to Brazil, where they arranged to have the Indians use them as molds over which to coagulate layers of rubber.

The second drawback was one that it took many years to overcome. If left in the vicinity of a hot stove, gum boots would gradually wilt, then grow nastily sticky, and finally collapse altogether into a mess rather like an overworked sample of bubble gum. If, on the other hand, the boots were put outside into the cold of a Salem winter, they would become hard and stiff, and sometimes brittle.

Science and experimentation had found answers to so many seemingly insoluble questions. Men expected confidently that if they tried hard enough and long enough, they would presently be able to find a way to avoid rubber's bad characteristics while retaining the good. With no previous similar undertaking to guide them, no remote appreciation of the intricate chemistry of the type of compounds we today call "elastomers," with nothing more than the absolute conviction that nothing could be beyond the powers of dedicated men, they slaved away.

Eventually, in the coal tar residue that was accumulating from the new gaslight industry, they found a solvent suitable for dissolving rubber. With the use of this, rubber might be separated from its grossest impurities and could eventually be remolded. It was presently found, too, that the consistency of the rubber product might be altered by mixing in varying quantities of other chemicals, notably sulfur, in a process we now call vulcanization. Discovered by Charles Goodyear in 1839 but not patented until 1844, this process would do little to relieve Goodyear's personal poverty or to make his family's life easier or happier. For men that came after him, the value was incalculable.

Rubber chemistry and manufacture is a long, long story by itself. Here it concerns us only insofar as its success made rubber desirable for thousands of new uses. Eventually it created such a demand for articles manufactured from the latex of the weeping tree that, in our twentieth century, the manager of a plantation in remote Central America had to begin each working day by gathering the precious seeds of his lone rubber tree. Because practically alone among the many trees that form milky and coagulable juices, *Hevea brasiliensis* has turned out to produce sufficient latex to make its cultivation profitable.

"In the discussion of rubber from its agricultural standpoint," says a United States Department of Agriculture bulletin issued in 1900, "it is of utmost importance to keep in mind . . . rubber is not like wheat, apples, or coffee, the produce of a single botanical species or group of closely allied species. It is comparable rather to sugar, a substance . . . obtainable from a great variety of plants, belonging to different botanical families, native to different parts of the earth and requiring utterly different conditions for their successful cultivation. . . . Substances marketed as rubber or gutta percha are known to exist in the milky juices of nearly two hundred plants belonging to botanical families quite as remote from each other as the sugar cane, the beet . . . and the sugar maple."

So the bouncing balls that Columbus saw in Haiti and Cortez in Mexico, though undoubtedly of rubber, probably could claim no connection with *Hevea brasiliensis*. It is to this Hevea, with its more generously flowing juice, and to the more resourceful natives of Brazil who found more practical uses for rubber than mere balls to play with, that we owe so much of our present civilization and most of this our story.

Within ten years after the first patent for vulcanization was granted, the demand for rubber had so increased that the lives of the rubber collectors — the *seringueiros* — on the upper Rio Negro far in the interior of Brazil, were being profoundly affected. Richard Spruce happened to be working in the region of the upper Rio Negro when the rubber boom first became a startling reality. In 1851 he left Manaos — then called Barra — for a four years' trip to the headwaters of that river and across the intervening plains to the upper reaches of the Orinoco.

"When I ascended the Rio Negro in 1851," he wrote in his journal, "I showed the inhabitants the abundance of rubber trees they possessed in their forests, and tried to induce them to set about its extraction, but they shook their heads and said it would never answer. At length the demand for rubber, especially from the United States, began to exceed the supply; the price consequently rose rapidly, until early in 1854 it reached the extraordinary price of . . . a little over five shillings a pound."

When, in 1855, Spruce came back down the river, he found it almost unrecognizable. "All the way down the Rio Negro the smoke was seen ascending from recently opened seringales [rubber smoking fires], principally in the islands. The extraordinary price reached by rubber in Pará in 1853 at length woke up the people from their lethargy. . . . Mechanics threw aside their tools, sugar-makers deserted their mills and Indians their roças. . . .

"The usual mode of drying the milk by smoke applied to successive coatings on a mould is followed by most rubber collectors."

Alfred Russel Wallace, another English botanist who was making collections in Brazil at about the same time, described the process in more detail: "For this purpose, an oval wooden spade is used, something like a canoe paddle but with a rather longer handle, the surface of which is made quite smooth. This is dipped in the bowl of rubbermilk, and each layer held over the smoke to dry. . . . This is repeated until a large mass is formed nearly twice as large as a man's head."

Removed by slitting along the edge of the paddles, these rubber balls were accumulated until they might be called for by one or another of the river steamers which plied the Amazon and its tributaries, and carried down river to exporters in Pará. In Pará the narrow streets along the waterfront were lined with piles of balls waiting for inspection. The smell of rubber filled the air. Rubber dominated everything in the city.

When the steamers arrived with their cargoes, rubber warehousemen worked ceaselessly day and night in sweltering heat and violent downpours. A single small steamer, in from the islands where she may have called at a hundred landings, might have picked up rubber from several hundred shippers consigned to perhaps eighty exporters. Inspectors were ceaselessly testing the balls for adulterants such as stones whose weight, it was hoped, might add to the price of the balls, which were paid for at so much per pound. Merchants haggled over prices of the inspected balls. While the rubber boom lasted, Pará was no sleepy tropical port.

In 1855 the fortunes of many men were dependent upon this rubber. Shipowners, steamer captains, storekeepers in the busy town or at the remote landings, middlemen, exporters — all these drew their livelihood, one way or another, from the rubber trade. In the midst of all the excitement, the poor, humble seringueiro and the rubber tree — "ciringa" to the natives — were all but forgotten. If the seringueiro ever complained, the outside world would not hear of it. And as for the trees, the jungle was so immense and the trees so many that few thought to look beyond the too demanding present into a future whose insistent demands might not be met.

In lands far from Brazil, more and more people were becoming dependent upon the things that could be made from rubber. As the cost of crude rubber soared and the supply was not increasing in pace with the demand, men of foresight began to worry about the world's continuing supply of a product gathered from wild trees in remote jungles. Not even the trackless jungle was endless. Just how many rubber trees might there really be? Would there always be enough? Would it always be gathered? Would it be shipped fast enough? Some day, in the foreseeable future, there might develop a shortage of ciringa trees or of seringueiros. What then?

Nobody in the land where the ciringa grew wild and belonged to the man who could tap it saw any need for expensive rubber plantations. But at Kew Gardens, where thinking had for years been along the lines of plant exploration and plant introduction, men were already considering plantation rubber a present necessity. Naturally enough, they thought of it in terms of a possible crop plant for tropical lands of the British Empire. As they had done with quinine, they were determined to tame rubber to plantation living.

The story of this taming begins with an unknown young Englishman who, in 1866, set forth from England to seek his fortune in more spacious lands and who, as lonely men often do, recorded his impressions in a journal. Strong, healthy, possessed of a jaw that jutted with determination, an observant eye, and an impressionable brain, twenty-year-old Henry Alexander Wickham was the very model of adventurous youth. Well educated, he could sketch, with an ease and effectiveness rare in our age of cameras, scenes that he found unusual or interesting. Or he could put his observations into words so vivid that stay-at-homes, reading them, would see and smell and feel the wild lands through which he had passed. His wants were simple and his curiosity about the world limitless. He could afford to take his time in looking over the tropical American lands where he proposed eventually to settle.

For three years he tried Central America but all the time felt the stronger pull of the continent to the south. He wanted to retrace the route the famous German naturalist, Alexander von Humboldt, had followed some seventy years before. Entering the mouth of the great river Orinoco in Venezuela, he would follow it to its source far away and high above in the rolling plains which also gave birth to the Rio Negro of the Amazon river system. Repute had it that in this high flat area there was a Rio Cassiquiare that formed a sort of canal between the two great river systems. Young Wickham proposed to cross from the Orinoco system into the Amazon system and follow this on down into Brazil.

Even well financed, it could not have been an easy trip. Without financial backing, it promised all sorts of delays and hardships. Yet a young man looking for ease and comfort would have stayed at home in England — and the future might well have been different for many other men. High in hopes, undismayed by difficulties —foreseen or imagined — Henry Wickham set out on the waters of the Orinoco in the early days of 1869.

"My original intention," he recorded in his journal for October 9, about nine months later, "had been to gain the Rio Negro but as my funds were getting uncomfortably low, I determined to recruit them somewhat ere attempting the descent into Brazil. I got two Indian peons and two boys from the Governador, to search the banks of the Orinoco for India Rubber."

The Englishman already knew the market value of India rubber; the natives were only beginning to learn it. When the boys he had contracted for did not arrive as expected, Wickham made a trip back to San Fernando to investigate. "San Fernando at noon," he recorded. "We found the whole of the inhabitants had been seized by a kind of mania for 'goma' [rubber] and were gone 'al monto' in search of it. The idea appeared to have struck them that it really must be a good thing if an Englishman like myself, coming from so far, desired to go in for it. . . .

"November 27th. . . . We arrived at the mouth of a small river called Caricia or Chirari. As this was about the neighbourhood I proposed to work India rubber during the drier weather, I camped. I at once despatched the men into the forest. . . . In a short time they returned with their notched sticks indicating fifty-seven trees seen in the small space of forest they had traversed."

We arrived! "We" meant Henry Wickham, the Indians working for him, and an English companion named Rogers, who, like Wickham, soon contracted malaria but who, unlike Wickham, became so completely incapacitated by it that he finally gave up the trip. Of course, had either of them thought enough, or known enough, to provide themselves with quinine, none of the party need have suffered. But in those days fever and ague were an expected part of tropical adventure and little was done to prevent it.

On a bluff above the clear waters of the river, the Indians put up a palm-thatched *rancho* that was to be Wickham's home for some months. Despite the crudeness of the shelter, the limited supplies, and the flies and mosquitoes that swarmed unceasingly during daylight hours, Wickham really loved it all. The world he looked out upon was practically the same that von Humboldt had viewed so long before and is hardly different today. Passing decades have changed almost beyond recognition our civilized world, but they have barely made an impression upon the jungle. Beautiful, fascinating, challenging, it is still the same untamed and untamable wilderness which the young Englishman of 1869 and 1870 gazed upon with never dimmed delight.

"I used to watch the cold shadows of night creep up from the water on the opposite side of the creek," he wrote, after recording at length his daytime misery with the insects, "and when the topmost boughs were alone tipped with golden light, I had the fires lit for supper. It was the only time of peace throughout the day. Then the long drawn notes of the Gallina del Monte sounded somewhat sadly from different directions of the forest . . . another singular note heard from the forest is made by a kind of rail. These birds appeared to assemble in numbers in swamps, especially when it threatened rain, for then they created such a clatter as to make the very woods resound. The ibis of the Orinoco is the most restless of birds, its cry of 'coro-coro' is heard at the first streak of dawn (whence its native name); and with quick flapping wings it flies down into the silent creek. Even when the moon rose late and all was still, save the occasional voice of an owl or tree frog, the sound of 'coro-coro' would ascend from the tree tops, as the bird took a sudden restless flight. The Indians say 'coro-coro' sleeps least of all birds."

During daylight hours, work went on steadily. "I continued clearing the trees daily in the forest," Wickham recorded, "and hoped to have 1000 ready for tapping in the ensuing month. One of the chief features is the variety and immense number of bush-ropes, 'bejucas,' forming a sort of natural cordage; they are of every size, and bind the top branches of the trees together, winding round the trunks, and coiling themselves on the ground in endless snakelike contortions. In some places they caused the men much trouble in cutting the paths with their machetes."

Working days were long. Each morning, before dawn, the men rose and made the rounds of the rubber trees, carefully making new diagonal gashes in the outer bark so that the latex might flow while the tree itself remained undamaged. Below each set of these gashes, the men attached a little cup which, for want of pottery or tin, they contrived out of smooth, tough plantain leaves. Later the latex was gathered, fires of palm nuts started, dipping of paddles and smoking of rubber, layer by layer, begun. With only brief pauses for rest, they continued this routine until daylight was swallowed up in encroaching jungle shadows.

"Sometimes, during the time for rest," so runs Wickham's journal, "I would sit and look up into the leafy arches above, and, as I gazed, become lost in the wonderful beauty of that upper system — a world of life complete within itself. This is the abode of strangely plumaged birds and elvish little *ti-ti* monkeys, which never descend to the dark, damp soil throughout their lives, but sing and gambol in the aerial gardens of dainty ferns and sweet-smelling orchids, for every tree supports an infinite variety of plant life. All above overhead seemed the very exuberance of animal and vegetable existence, and below, its contrast, decay and darkness. Here and there was a mass of orchids, carried from above by the fall of some withered branch, sickening into pallor, thrust out from vitalizing light and air."

On Christmas Day, 1869, possibly more than a little lonely and homesick, he wrote in a less exalted tone, "There was small chance of oversleeping the dawn, for with it came mosquitoes and they did not desist from annoying until dark. . . . My hands and feet again became very sore and inflamed from the constant irritation of these plagues. Daily wishing for the night is not a very satisfactory way of living."

Satisfactory or not, Wickham stayed on, enduring the misery, increasingly enthralled by the life around him: monkeys large and small, snakes that usually fled from men in terror, jaguars whose presence could only be guessed by their numberless tracks. Wickham's real worry, though, was caused by the scant yield of rubber. The first hundred trees tapped were most disappointing and the young Englishman concluded what was later to prove the fact: that the weeks during which rubber trees were loaded with green fruit would be the time when latex yields must be poor. In fact, it would be the only time during the whole year when rubber could not profitably be collected. Wickham was already starting on his career as expert in tropical agriculture and an authority on rubber growing. Fifty years later, this would bring him as reward a knighthood.

At the camp on the Caricia, though, Wickham could gladly have traded his chances of future glory for a present supply of ammunition. "We should have lived well here," he wrote, "but that my ammunition was fast giving out, so we were unable to kill much game. Fish could be hooked in the river, turtle eggs dug up from the warm sands along its banks, but monkeys, deer, wild hogs, birds — so plentiful and such delightful eating — were becoming increasingly unobtainable.

"This Lent I had no need to observe the fast," he wrote on Good Friday, "for it was of necessity; there was nothing but a little, very little fish to be had, my ammunition being long since exhausted."

The insects, however, observed no fast. Fevers continued to sap the strength of Englishmen and Indians alike. Then the rains started — not the nice gentle rains of a temperate April but the vindictive downpours of tropical wet seasons. Soon the waterlogged land could not hold the water and the rivers rose rapidly. At the end of the month, Wickham "evacuated [his] position as no longer tenable, intending to make a push for Pará by way of the Cassiquiare, Don Carlos, and Manaos."

Magic names! Pará — the port at the mouth of the Amazon where La Condamine ended his cross-continent journey, where Richard Spruce had first landed, through which rubber articles had first emerged from the jungles to come to the attention of the rest of the world! Manaos — the bustling city at the junction of the Amazon and the Rio Negro, some thousand miles from the ocean yet a port for ocean-going vessels and a rival of jealous Pará! Here, in 1855, Richard Spruce first noted the start of the rubber boom. And the Cassiquiare? Seek for it on your map and you may find, if your eyes are good and you have sufficient patience, a little wavy line connecting the upper reaches of the Orinoco with the headwaters of the Rio Negro across the high flat lands of Venezuela. A raindrop falling there would seem to have an equal chance of ending its earthly journey in the Caribbean near Trinidad or in the Atlantic Ocean beyond the mouth of the Amazon — granted, of course, that the heat of the tropical lowlands through which it must pass has not again drawn it up into the ever hovering rainclouds.

The boats were covered over with thatches of palm fronds to protect them and their passengers from the rains; the ciringa trees were tapped for the last time, the last balls of latex smoked and packed into the boats. But when they started the journey, the laden boats were too heavy to be navigated upstream against the current by men still weak from fevers and undernourishment.

Reluctantly abandoning his plans to journey into the Cassiquiare, Wickham headed back downstream to San Fernando, where he hoped to be able to attach himself to one of the companies of Venezuelan gentlemen who, now and again, journeyed into Brazil on trading expeditions. He found such a group and they agreed to let him accompany them. They were, however, in no hurry and did not get started before the end of June, over a month later.

"Next morning, I woke at the first crow of the cocks from the solitary lodge," Wickham wrote of the dawn of their departure. "I never now hear the crow of a cock ringing shrilly out on the morning air, but I think of many a start I have made in some dim, unknown, moonlit path in the *mañana por la madenga* before dawn."

Up river, portaging across the tablelands, down over into the Rio Negro itself, portaging again around the falls, the party finally arrived on September 3 in the thriving river port of Manaos where ocean-going steamers, some of British registry, were tied up. Perhaps the sight of these gave the young Englishman a few twinges of homesickness. Yet never for a moment did he consider booking passage home on any of them.

Like so many men before and since, Henry Wickham had fallen completely under the spell of the tropics and of those lush, dim, moonlit paths which must be explored. To him, the valley of the Amazon offered both adventure and opportunity and there he made plans to settle for — as then he expected — the remainder of his life. "I purpose," he wrote, "to make the tablelands in the triangle betwixt the Tapajos [River] and the Amazon, behind the town of Santarem, in the future the base of my operations."

As it happened, the journal which Wickham had kept so carefully throughout his trip came to the attention of the British consul in Pará, who insisted it should be published and himself saw it through press. So, in 1872, Henry Alexander Wickham's *Rough Notes of a Journey Through the Wilderness* appeared in England and came to the attention of the director of Kew Gardens.

Sir Joseph Hooker had succeeded his father as director of the Gardens in 1865. As he read Wickham's book, he became impressed with the young man's keenly observant eye, his vivid descriptions, his delicate sketches of jungle scenes and plants and, in particular, of the leaves and fruit of the ciringa tree. From these sketches and from dried specimens that found their way to Kew, Sir Joseph was finally able to place the rubber tree in its proper botanical place. Previously called *Siphonia elastica,* it became then — and for all time, apparently — *Hevea brasiliensis.*

This interest in the rubber tree was nothing new for Sir Joseph. It had long been one of his dreams to procure seeds of the Hevea so that plantations of rubber might be started in the East Indies and India itself. He had already made one attempt, but the seeds sent from Brazil died during the long, hot sea voyage, so that the effort was wasted. He must try again.

As Sir Joseph Hooker read of young Wickham's journey and of his rubber collecting on the banks of the Caricia, it occurred to him that here was the very man he needed — brave, resourceful, acquainted with the land and with the trees. He wrote to his young countryman a letter that, many weeks later, was delivered at the new plantation he was working upon near Santarem. Would Wickham, the letter begged, secure rubber seeds for Kew Gardens and the Government of India, and would he get the seeds to Kew while they were still viable? No means were suggested, no directions given. As Wickham expressed it, "Nothing was said of means whereby either of these was to be accomplished. A straight offer to do it; pay to follow result."

With that opportunity, the question came home to Wickham, how in earth to bring it off. He knew that for a long time past, Sir Joseph Hooker had been trying to, but with no success.

To collect rubber seeds would be the least problem for a planter in Santarem. He knew Hevea when he saw it, had an expert's eye for fine, tall, high-yielding trees. He knew where they grew on the tablelands above the Tapajos River and he knew when the fruit was due to ripen and the seeds fall. He could converse with the Indians easily and knew how to win their co-operation. So, up to that point, he had no worries.

What did worry him was how to pack the seeds he should collect, how to find prompt and speedy passage to England, how to provide for proper care of the seeds during that passage. Delicate, oily seeds which easily turned rancid and died must not be stowed away in the hot, stuffy hold of a ship, but must be kept where air could circulate freely and where the rats could not. The problem was not so much to find the seeds as to find the right ship and the right shipmaster.

There was also the question of how the port might be successfully cleared. Since the days of the Spanish Conquest, South American officials had been accustomed to referring all matters of policy, even seemingly trivial ones, to the headquarters of a highly centralized government. When the center of government was in Spain or Portugal, important matters might wait years for decisions while questions and answers made their slow way back and forth across a wide ocean. Men whom these decisions concerned might grow old and die before the final answer came.

Now, many decades after South America had won her independence, each republic had its own highly centralized government and the process was speeded up, though only in a comparative sense. Wickham knew perfectly well that no port official would feel free to come to any independent decision on any matter for which there was not already an accepted precedent. Since the shipment of rubber seeds was an entirely new matter, there would be no telling how long the delicate cargo might have to wait in the moist heat of Pará while officials argued with one another and with their superiors in

Rio de Janeiro and, like the Venezuelan gentleman in whose company Wickham had traveled, took their time about coming to a final decision.

There was no law on the books that prohibited the exportation of rubber seeds. But suppose some of the officials or their friends derived their incomes from the rubber trade, as was only too likely in a rubber port. And suppose they saw in the shipment of seeds a threat to their source of income! Suppose they just decided to forbid the export or to impose an exorbitantly high export tax. Or suppose that they finally decided that the fate of a few thousand rubber seeds could be no concern of theirs! In the end, it wouldn't matter — not if the ship had to remain anchored in the heat of Pará while they came to the decision.

The main preoccupation of the collector, then, was to figure out some way of getting the seed to England quickly and safely. As the season of ripening rubber fruit drew on, the problem became more urgent. Then luck played into young Wickham's hands.

The Inman Steamship Line was inaugurating a new service — Liverpool to the upper Amazon direct — and the first ship of this service, the *Amazonas,* steamed proudly up into Santarem and dropped anchor off the town. To celebrate, all the European planters of the vicinity were invited on board for dinner and an evening's entertainment. The two supercargoes in charge made delightful hosts, the dinner was excellent, the wine superb, the entertainment all that the guests might have dreamed of. Everyone was proud to be a part of this great celebration.

The next day the planters went back to their toil and the ship moved on up the river to Manaos, some five hundred miles above. Then, bit by bit, strange news trickled back. Those charming supercargoes had become charming rogues — had sold the ship's cargo, pocketed the profits, and disappeared without a trace into the wide wilderness. The ship's captain found himself without supercargoes, with empty coffers, and no way of purchasing a profitable cargo for the return voyage.

Faced with disaster, Captain Murray might accept an offer that, under other circumstances, he would have spurned. Henry Wickham immediately saw the heaven-sent opportunity. He would charter the ship for his rubber seeds. And because he had no funds — everything of his own having been sunk in the new plantation which could neither be sold nor mortgaged profitably — he took the bold plunge of chartering the *Amazonas* in the name of the Government of India. Since Captain Murray was in no position to question how completely the young planter represented the Government of India, he wrote back from Manaos that he would meet Wickham at the appointed time at the junction of the Amazon and Tapajos rivers.

The fruit was already ripening in the forest and there was no time to lose. Wickham secured a small Indian canoe, moved in it swiftly up the right bank of the Tapajos, then made the crossing, so difficult for a small canoe in a great river. From the left bank, he struck back into the jungles towards the higher, flatter lands where the Hevea grew strong and tall, measuring from ten to twelve feet in circumference.

"Working with as many Tapuyo Indians as I could get together on short notice," he reminisced many years later, "I daily ranged the forest, and packed on our backs in Indian pannier baskets as heavy loads of seed as we could march down under. I was working against time."

The Indian village maids were drafted to weave openwork baskets where carefully dried seed would be packed between layers of dried plantain leaves. They slung the filled baskets from the rafters of Indian ranchos where ventilation would be good yet where neither greedy birds nor prowling animals could reach them. When the date appointed for meeting the *Amazonas* drew near, Wickham had his baskets carefully stowed under the palm-thatched shelter of his canoe, which then floated downstream to Captain Murray's ship.

The Captain, of course, was in no very cheerful mood. A fine end to his first trip up the Amazon, he told himself sourly as he watched his young countryman making such a fuss over a silly cargo of seeds. Fast service — Liverpool to the upper Amazon — indeed! And now returning home as nursemaid to a few thousand seeds! Would he ever live it down?

Henry Wickham, however, was not asking the Captain to nurse his seeds. The least he could do, after he had risked all in chartering the ship, was to see the seeds safe in Kew. So he left his new plantation and the tablelands between the rivers which he had "purposed to make in the future the base of operations" and took passage along with his precious seeds. He must still face the customs officials in Pará before he could get them out of Brazil.

The question of how to arrange matters in Pará haunted him all the way down the river. But when the *Amazonas* dropped anchor off Pará to get her clearance papers, he knew the time for action was at hand. He went to the British consul and talked over his problem; then the two together paid a visit to the port official upon whose attitude so much depended.

The port official was charmed with the sun-tanned square-jawed young Englishman who loved Brazil enough to propose to make his home there. That he had manners to pay a courtesy call upon the port official before leaving for a trip home was very much to his credit. So the three chatted easily, without any apparent hurry.

"A fascinating land," the young man murmured. "I have hoped to make my home here. And now, on this visit to England, I would also hope to show my people something of the beauties of Brazil."

The official smiled appreciatively, "Of course, Senhor."

"It has seemed to me," Wickham pursued, "that there should be a suitable collection of Brazilian plants in Her Majesty's Royal Botanic Gardens at Kew. Do you not agree, Senhor?"

"Her Majesty's Gardens at Kew?" the gentleman repeated. "Of course. Everyone has heard of them — surely Brazil should be represented there."

The young man looked grave and added sadly, "If only the trip were not so long — the heat here in Pará so injurious to plants . . ."

"Perhaps a trifle warm," the gentleman agreed, mopping his brow.

"Delightful — the climate — only a little hard on delicate botanical specimens stored in the hold of a ship where none of these fresh sea breezes can reach them."

"You mean to say you actually have such specimens with you?"

"A waste of effort, I'm sure," the young man agreed by a nod of the head. "Still I have wished to make the try even though there is small likelihood of their arriving alive."

"Surely, if you do not delay here in the port — "

"Ah, but delay cannot be avoided. Clearance papers cannot be hurried."

"Ah, but they can — if I give the orders. How soon can you make ready to depart?"

Young Wickham hesitated just long enough to appear to give the matter grave consideration. He knew, though, that steam was up in the boilers of the ship because he had particularly requested Captain Murray to keep ready for instant departure.

"That," he murmured, "would be for Captain Murray to say. Still, I believe he has not yet allowed the men shore leave, so if the boilers are still warm — and I think they must be so short a time after arrival — we could leave almost at once, with your so gracious permission, Senhor."

"A toast, then, to your speedy departure and safe arrival in England!"

Within the hour, the *Amazonas* steamed out of Pará harbor. Once in the wider spaces of the great Amazon delta, Wickham had his openwork baskets removed from the stuffy hold and hung up where fresh sea breezes could easily reach them. The passage was as speedy and safe as the Brazilian port official might have wished. Forewarned by a special message sent from a southern port of England, Sir Joseph Hooker had a freight train waiting at the London dockside when the *Amazonas* tied up there. Without delay, the precious cargo was rushed to Kew.

Two weeks later, in the Kew greenhouses, some seven thousand seedlings of *Hevea brasiliensis* began pushing their slender green tips through the brown earth of the seedbeds. Today the men who worked so hard to bring this about are long since gone, but some of those very seedlings are now raising their proud, tall heads in rubber plantations of India or Burma or Ceylon. And from their own seeds, many another plantation has sprung.

It is many years since the rubber plantations of the East Indies have produced sufficient rubber to compete with that from the ancestral sources. And saddest for Brazil, it soon turned out that the seringueiros of the Far East could live on even lower incomes than the poor, often pitied Brazilian rubber collectors. The greatest years of the Brazilian rubber boom lasted from about 1880 to 1910. In 1910, Brazil exported approximately 38,500 tons of rubber worth 377,000 cruzeiros on the world's markets. By 1921, the export had shrunk to 17,000 tons, valued at only 36,000 cruzeiros. Half the crop for one-tenth the price! The rubber boom was broken.

Manaos, the onetime bustling center of the rubber barons' domains — whose costly opera house, as luxurious as the best in Europe, drew Europe's best opera stars — is now just another rather sleepy river port. Rubber no longer dominates Pará. People talk condemningly of the "big steal" of rubber seeds perpetrated by Henry Wickham more than eighty years ago. Yet those who condemn do not tell us where our present civilization might be had it not been for the reliable supplies of plantation rubber which began with the trees that "stolen" seed produced.

We learned the answer to this the hard way during World War II when so much of our supply of Eastern plantation rubber was cut off. While shortages mounted desperately and rigid rationing was enforced, botanists left their laboratories and herbaria to comb the American tropics for stands of rubber trees and to help revive the almost lost art of the seringueiro.

Brazil now has her own rubber plantations where rubber growing is a big business. Plantation owners and seringueiros are now only a small part of the picture. Plantation managers, horticulturists, plant breeders, plant pathologists have taken up where the plant hunter left off. Here, even more than with cinchona, which is expected to die when the crop is harvested, grafting has become very important. A high-yielding trunk is grafted to roots resistant to diseases that may be borne in the soil. Then still another graft — this one especially resistant to leaf infections — is fixed to the top of the trunk. In this weird manner are produced the needed healthy, high-yielding trees required for plantation life.

For, even in these days of synthetic rubbers, plantation rubber is still a vital product. In fact, all rubber, whatever its source, is vital. There can hardly be too much. So perhaps it is no longer necessary, as it was in 1925, for the manager of an experimental farm in Central America to hoard the seeds of a lone rubber tree grown from a "stolen" seed produced in the East Indies by another tree which, in turn, sprang from a seed "stolen" in 1876 from the jungles above the Rio Tapajos in central Brazil.

VII

Enough Rope

CAPTAINS OF YANKEE SHIPS had, in 1824, been among the first to see in the crude rubber boots of the Brazilian Indians articles that might prove to be of commercial value in Yankee ports. Ever on the alert for profitable opportunities, Yankee trading ships continued for many decades to sail the seas. A brave sight they must have been, those ships, with their spreading white sails and their intricate tracery of rope rigging.

Though their day of greatness is long past, men still grow poetic over their memory.

An incredible amount of rope went into those ships. Each great sail was edged with rope and was held in place by ropes. Ropes gave the sailor toeholds along the spars and fashioned the ladders up which they clambered when they went aloft. Ropes formed the towlines of harpoons on the whaling ships out of New Bedford and Nantucket. On all ships, ropes were fashioned into the cargo-loading nets which yet other ropes raised and lowered. Ropes up to twenty-one inches around held the anchors which had to be used in open roadsteads. At docksides, ropes were needed to warp the ships into their berths.

Naturally, then, the soundness of a ship's ropes was hardly less important than the soundness of her construction. Hemp, a fiber prepared from the stems of a common plant named *Cannabis sativa,* had long been used in the ropewalks of both Britain and America. Here yarn was "spun," strands "formed," and rope "laid," to use the ropemakers' technical language. You could lay good enough rope of hemp if you handled it properly. If you kept it tarred against damage by salt sea water, it would last quite well though the tarring made it both heavy and dirty. Still, there was nothing to be done about it.

At least there was nothing to be done with the old familiar hemp ropes. Then, in 1820, Lieutenant John White of the U.S. Navy brought back to Salem, Massachusetts, from the Philippine Islands a sample of an unfamiliar fiber which men then called "Manila hemp" — now shortened to "Manila." The same Yankee imagination that had seen the possibilities in rubber perceived the value of this new blond fiber — cleaner, lighter, stronger, and, wonder of wonders, practically undamaged by sea water even when untarred. Within four years, the new fiber was being used extensively in the rope-walks of Salem and Boston. Though British ships would long remain loyal to the old familiar tarred hemp, American ships were soon demanding and, insofar as supply permitted, getting ropes made of Manila.

It was not a recently discovered plant, this Manila. Antonio Pigafetta, who accompanied Magellan in 1521 when he discovered the Philippines, had drawn up a list of the "words of these heathen people." On the list was included: "For the cloth with which they cover themselves — abacá." In 1686 the English captain William Dampier described the production and use of this "plantain fibre." And of course, the Spaniards whose possessions the Islands were, mentioned it now and again in their writings of the seventeenth and eighteenth centuries.

Yet only in the nineteenth century — 1818, to be exact — was the first commercial shipment of abacá fiber made from the Philippines. The total for that year was a mere 41 tons. Ten years later, 276 tons were exported. The year's total for 1850 was 8500 tons; for 1900, nearly 90,000 tons.

The abacá plant — *Musa textilis,* to use its scientific name — belongs to the banana family and looks so much like its fruit-bearing cousin that, until the fruit itself appears, only an expert can tell the plants apart. Abacá also forms finger-like fruit — which is edible if you want to fill your mouth with hard, angular seeds while you eat it. But the only people who would grow abacá for its fruit are those who might be interested in crossbreeding it with other members of the same plant family to find out what strange new characteristics might appear in the crossbred stock.

Like the familiar but unrelated day lilies, most members of the banana family propagate themselves by underground stems. In fact, like *Musa sapientum,* whose seedless fruit we eat, most have no choice in the matter. New plants spring up from buds that appear at intervals along the intricate network of underground stems — the mat — that forms the basis of a mature banana or abacá plantation. Sections cut from such stems — "rhizomes" is the technical term — are used to start new plantations. The new plants, being in a sense an extension of the old, closely resemble the mother plant, whereas plants grown from seed must have a questionable mixed inheritance. So plantation managers, interested only in high yields of fiber, start new plantings with rhizomes from their highest-yielding plants.

A mature plantation of abacá or banana is an impressive sight. The tall green plants rival in height some of the lesser forest trees, so that a man standing among the great soaring clumps of leaves feels as dwarfed as might a field mouse in a bed of cannas. Plant debris litters the ground, which is so shaded that little underbrush will grow. A strange greenish light is over all. The air is hot and steamy and breathless and quite still save when a breeze above on the outside moves across the tops of the leaves and rustles them gently.

High winds play havoc with the fruit-bearing Musa. The great, smooth, rounded leaves — as long as a man is tall — are torn along the crosswise veins until they hang in shreds from the midrib. As they increase in violence, these winds break down leaf and flower and fruit stalks until whole plantations may be flattened and a year's crop destroyed in the space of a few minutes. The banana is a fragile plant. The taller, stronger *Musa textilis* is better equipped to survive tropical hurricanes, for each leaf stem is provided with the fiber-bearing sheath which gives it its value as a crop plant.

This abacá seems to be native only in the area of the Philippines and adjacent islands, where it grows wild. A choosy plant, it found conditions of soil and climate just right in the hill country of southern Luzon and of Mindanao. Here, before recorded history, natives found it, discovered the value of its fibers, and decided it might be convenient to have such plants growing near their homes. They cleared away some jungle trees, dug holes here and there, dropped a piece of an abacá rhizome into each hole, and left the rest to nature. Since the soil was right and the moist heat of the climate just what abacá plants needed, it really wasn't asking much of nature. The plants throve and soon repaid the cultivators for their small labors. They had all the fiber they needed for ropes and hammocks and fishnets, and even clothing, with perhaps a little left over to sell to less industrious neighbors.

Spanish explorers and settlers who began going to the Islands in the sixteenth century could not fail to see the value of abacá as a crop plant. More familiar with systematic agriculture than the primitive natives, they applied more method to the growing of abacá and made a greater effort to keep plantations clear from shrubs and grass that otherwise might compete with abacá for light and nourishment. They saw no need to make a profounder study of the best conditions for growing abacá. Their fiber had no serious competitor in the world's markets, they could sell every bit they raised and they could raise enough to live quite well off the income, so why worry about more!

For centuries no one made any further effort to improve methods of cultivation or the quality of fibers. Then, in the closing weeks of 1898, the Spanish-American War came to an end and the Islands passed from Spanish dominion to that of the United States. The new administrators, shocked by the poverty of many of the natives, sought ways to help them improve their living conditions. For an agricultural people, the answer must lie in more and better crops — rice, copra [coconut], and abacá, to name the most important.

If new plantations were to prove more successful and profitable than the old, they must not be started in the old haphazard manner. A systematic study must be undertaken and answers to important questions found. In what kind of soil did abacá grow best? And what of climatic conditions? Where might the highest-yielding fiber plants be located? Rhizomes for new plantations must be cut from these. Then there was the question of short-term crops to be planted between the rows of rhizomes, to keep the soil under cultivation and to yield the planters some profit while they waited the two years required to produce a profitable crop of abacá.

Southern Davao — still only superficially tamed after so many centuries of European occupation of the Islands — appeared to be an area ideally suited for starting the projected new plantations. Lieutenant Bolton, in 1899 first American governor of Davao, gradually brought peace to the people and persuaded them to end their feuds and settle down to raise marketable crops like abacá. By the time he met his death at the hands of a treacherous native chieftain, he had also managed to interest other Americans in starting large-scale abacá plantations on Davao.

Plantation life in the remoter tropics is never the easy, romantic life storytellers delight in picturing. It is incredibly difficult when the plantations have to be cut out of the virgin bush. Forest giants, whose hard-fibered wood can turn the edge of the best steel cutting instruments, must be removed. Underbrush, which shoots up again almost before the cutter's back is turned, must be kept cleared away. A house must be built where only the crudest building materials are easily available. Every product of manufacture, from nails to roofing, is brought in at tremendous expense of time, energy, and money. For that house must be a home — must provide a substitute for all that is left behind thousands of miles away. It must offer some feeble compensation for the haunting loneliness of remote plantation life where a familiar face is rare and a familiar tongue rarer still.

The American planters who came to Davao would not remain satisfied with old methods of cultivation. They decided that legumes, which could enrich the soil by the nitrogenous products they produced, should make better short-term crops than the traditional sweet potatoes. When their abacá matured and they could watch the natives laboriously stripping the fibers from the leaf stalks by hand, they realized this old method was wasteful, slow, and expensive. So they devised machines for stripping, had them built, and installed them in their stripping sheds. Everything was booming in the abacá business. Supply increased and improved, demand grew too, and everyone should have been happy.

But not everyone was happy. For abacá buyers realized increasingly the unhappy fact that Manila was half a world away from the markets which had come to depend upon the crop that still was practically a monopoly of the Philippine Islands. Moreover, citizens of other Oriental lands were moving in to start new plantations or to buy up old ones that might come on the market. Control of a vital crop was passing to alien hands.

It began in the early days of expansion when the available supply of Philippine labor proved insufficient to cope with the increasing demands of the Islands' three paying crops. Japanese laborers were encouraged to immigrate. Hardworking, thrifty, hoarding their wages, many remained to buy the plantations upon which, at first, they had worked. Prosperous Japanese at home, seeing in abacá a highly profitable investment, also bought plantations. Japanese plant scientists and fiber specialists were sent out from Japan. Chinese merchants gradually became the middlemen who bought the stripped and washed fibers and resold them advantageously on the world's markets. Presently the American planters who remained in the abacá-growing business discovered they were very much in the minority.

Long before the disastrous events of Pearl Harbor, people at home in the States began to grow alarmed. Rope — good, strong, reliable rope — was vital to so many industries. Yet any war that might involve countries with Pacific interests and powerful navies could cut off our supply of Manila fiber at its source.

Men had already attempted to grow abacá outside of the Philippines in other lands of the Pacific area; also in India. When these attempts failed, their failure seemed to prove that abacá could grow nowhere save in the Islands. Botanists, of course, could hardly accept such an idea. Given similar conditions of soil, of nourishment and drainage, of climate and of the critical balance between hours of darkness and of daylight that exists in the tropics, a plant should not concern itself with the precise longitude where it was set out. To convince non-botanists of this would take many years of painstaking study and discouraging effort.

In 1901, abacá seeds were first sent to the western hemisphere from the Philippine island of Negros. Planted outdoors in Florida and in the United States Department of Agriculture greenhouses in Washington, D.C., not a single one germinated. Early in the following year, seeds were sent to Puerto Rico and again none germinated. In October 1902, seeds planted in the Washington greenhouses yielded eighty-nine seedlings. These seedlings were distributed to Florida, the Hawaiian Islands, and to several Caribbean islands. Some died at once; all soon disappeared.

The same sad story of failure was repeated again and again during the years between 1904 and 1911. Of all the attempted plantings, not a single abacá survived to maturity. Yet to the people who murmured, "We told you so — this proves abacá will grow nowhere save in the Philippine Islands!" botanists still insisted, "It proves nothing except that we have not yet solved the problem. Give us time to study it further and we'll solve it yet."

In March 1911, another shipment of seeds, this time packed in charcoal, arrived in Washington. The twelve hundred seedlings that sprouted were once more distributed to planters in the American tropics — Cuba, Puerto Rico, Nicaragua, Costa Rica, Panama, and Mexico — who had them set out, then promptly forgot about them. No one concerned with the necessity for producing Manila in America had taken the trouble to convince these planters that the seedlings, properly cared for, might one day develop into highly profitable new crop plants. So the plantings were neglected, the plants ignored or destroyed. From all the years of effort, there resulted only one or two old mats of abacá gone wild in Almirante, Panama, where they were rediscovered in 1925. Possibly, but not certainly, a few others of the 1911 distribution survived in Puerto Rico.

By 1921 our government's fiber experts were growing seriously alarmed. "The average annual consumption of abacá fiber in the United States for the past 12 years," wrote one of these experts in a report published in 1921, "has been approximately 72,000 tons. This amount is about half the world production of this fiber. The principal uses of abacá fiber in the United States are for the manufacture of well drilling cables, and transmission rope." The chief users included the U.S. Navy, the merchant marine, oil-drilling and construction companies. None of these could be hampered by rope shortage without damage to our whole national economy.

"The entire world supply of abacá fiber," the report stated, "is now produced in the Philippine Islands. . . . The existing abacá situation is a striking instance of having 'all our eggs in one basket', with that basket on the opposite side of the world." The risks of war were pointed out — also the risk that increasing alien control of the crop might make things difficult when, eventually, the United States would give up political control of the islands.

Most alarming of all was a danger that no biologist could afford to overlook. Like animals, plants can sicken and die of infectious diseases. Suppose that some plant disease, such as the one that was already seriously interfering with banana production in Central America, got started in just one Philippine abacá plantation. The government of the Islands had very limited facilities for the detection and control of plant diseases. Besides, abacá grew wild, so that even the most careful inspection of plantations could not hope to eradicate any disease, once it had contaminated plants scattered throughout the dense jungles. Borne through the warm, moist air by winds or by insects that flew from plant to plant, infections would spread quickly. Not only did all the world's supply of abacá grow in the Philippines, but it grew there within a disturbingly narrow area. Unless plantations could be started in other parts of the world, that world might someday be deprived of all abacá by a disaster similar to that which has now eliminated every mature tree of our North American chestnuts.

The experts had a plan. Conditions of soil and climate and moisture should be studied in those districts where the best fiber grew. Then the American tropics should be surveyed to locate areas where conditions for growth might be most similar. Then, and only then, rhizomes from the best stock of the Philippines should be selected for shipment to Central America. Men with experience in growing that other Musa, the banana, should handle this shipment.

At last, in December 1921, a real start was being made upon a project that, twenty years later to the month, would save all non-Pacific lands from a disastrous shortage of cordage. Five days after the attack on Pearl Harbor, a conference on cordage was called in Washington, to discuss ways and means of meeting the long-dreaded crisis. The next week rapid expansion of abacá plantings in Central America was under way.

This meant, of course, that abacá was already growing in some Central American plantations and in sufficient quantity to provide rhizomes for the expansion. It meant, too, that someone had acquired the know-how to pick suitable land for abacá plantings and to cultivate the plantings, once they were made. In fact, it meant that throughout the discouraging years some men had kept their faith in abacá as a crop plant for the American tropics and had seen to it that the high-yielding abacá which, in 1925, had finally come into their hands was not allowed to die of neglect as had previous plantings.

In December 1921, the handwriting was already on the wall for all intelligent men to read. Newspapers were printing propaganda against permitting the exportation of seed or rhizomes from the Philippines. Chambers of Commerce were loud in their support of this attitude. It was the old, old story of a land wanting to keep a profitable monopoly, of planters who feared what might happen to their incomes if their crop became naturalized in other lands. In December 1925, the Philippine legislature passed the law that was to guard the Philippine monopoly of abacá.

Fortunately, though, just three months before the law was passed, a large consignment of living plants, rhizomes, and seeds was shipped from Davao to Central America. Fortunately, too, this final shipment proved successful. But it had been touch and go. A 1923 shipment of cuttings of four desirable abacá varieties had reached the Panama Canal Zone so infested with root borers and nematodes that the United Fruit Company decided to receive no further shipments, though it had originally undertaken to get the new plantations started. It could well be a risky thing for a company whose business was the growing and shipping of bananas to introduce into the crop area infected seedlings of another plant so closely related to bananas. The same nematodes and root borers might find themselves equally at home in the fruit-bearing Musa.

The next year, abacá suckers were collected in southern Luzon, shipped to Manila, transhipped to a steamer bound for Seattle, then placed in freight cars destined for Maryland. The few plants that survived the long journey and the many handlings in transit died shortly after being planted in the Maryland greenhouses.

Everyone knew time was running out. Any day the Philippine legislature might act. Yet, with nothing but failure to record, there were still men who refused to give up. They still believed that "clean" material could be secured and packed and shipped in such a way that healthy abacá plantings might result. They even persuaded the United Fruit Company to give abacá another try.

Early in 1925 one of the company pathologists went to the

Philippines to locate new varieties of the fruit-bearing Musa to try in Panama, where the disease called "Panama wilt" was threatening large areas of banana plantings with complete destruction. The hope was that somewhere, possibly in the Islands, a disease-resistant fruit stock might be found. But if the fruit crop was to disappear as a big business from the American tropics, it might be that abacá could provide a profitable substitute — that is, if by some lucky chance it proved to be disease-resistant.

The company pathologist, then, was instructed to look over abacá plantations and, if possible, to bring back disease-free material with which to start abacá plantations in Panama.

This was a matter that required diplomatic as well as scientific skill, for the Manila newspapers were daily insisting that the exportation of abacá growing stock would impoverish the Islands and ruin all planters. Wisely deciding not to argue the question, the pathologist approached one planter after another, presented his problems, explained the needs, asked for co-operation. This, finally, he received from two American-born planters — Henry Peabody and Charles Harvey — who owned large tracts of land along the Gulf of Davao. Recognizing the risks to their own personal fortunes, they also could recognize the greater risk that failure to co-operate might mean to a world grown dependent upon good cordage fiber. To do this required vision and courage of a truly high order.

These men had holdings scattered all along the ninety-mile Gulf of Davao. No single plantation contained all the varieties of abacá that might be desirable to try abroad. Sturdiness, high fiber yield, freedom from disease — these were the qualities sought. During June, July, and most of August, the work of selecting, cutting, and shipping rhizomes to a central point went on. At Malita, on the coast, the pathologist examined each plant individually to make sure no plant disease or insects were present.

Knowing this would certainly be their last chance, the men performed their tasks with great thoroughness. Every possible method of transporting abacá was considered. Four hundred rhizomes were planted in whatever containers the remote tropical plantation could afford — old packing boxes or five-gallon gasoline tins with the tops cut off. Other rhizomes were crated. Seeds were packed in tins of charcoal which helped keep them from spoiling. Bunches of mature abacá fruit were put in the ship's cold storage. When finally ready, the shipment included 1438 items of plant material, packed in 279 containers, selected from 6 choice varieties of abacá.

Malita is an open roadstead with no facilities for docking ocean freighters. Big ships must drop anchor offshore while shallow draft lighters ferry back and forth from plantation docks. All cargo is loaded from dock to lighter and from lighter to ship. It's not easy even on a smooth sea, and the cargo is likely to get shaken up in the process. On a rough sea, loading is next to impossible.

While the men at Malita waited impatiently for the expected freighter to appear, the skies grew dark, promising a storm. Then, early one morning, the *Ethan Allen* and her accompanying lighter hove in sight. Miraculously, the skies seemed to clear. Everyone turned to at once to get the cargo aboard. All day and into the night they worked until every item was in place. The less heavy boxes of plants in sphagnum were put on the upper boat deck, heavier boxes containing dirt on the hatch covers, crates of rhizomes and tins of seeds in the poop cargo space. Long after dark, the twentieth-century *Bounty* sailed away.

Like the breadfruit of the *Bounty,* the abacá plants of the

Ethan Allen would find their worst enemy in the salt sea spray. And though the *Ethan Allen* was a far larger ship, other cargo requirements made it impossible for her to carry fresh water in sufficient quantities to keep the abacá leaves hosed off. The stormy weather, which had so obligingly held off while the ship was loading, returned and settled about the ship as soon as she emerged from the Gulf of Davao. It stayed with her during most of the long crossing. Ship's officers obligingly helped move the plants from above decks to the holds. As great waves broke over the decks, some salt spray penetrated beneath the hatches and into the dark, unventilated holds where the plants were already suffering. Crates shifted and crushed some plants. Many times it looked as if the last shipment of abacá might prove as useless as the first.

On October 3, after a voyage of forty-two days, the *Ethan Allen* steamed into the port of Balboa at the Pacific end of the Panama Canal. She entered the Canal, made her slow way through the up locks to Gatun Lake and down through the locks to Cristobal where the *Parismina* of the United Fruit Company was waiting to take the plants on the last leg of their journey, to the Plant Quarantine Station on Columbus Island near Bocas del Toro, Panama. For the last time, the plant shipment must be moved — to another lighter and then ashore. And here again they narrowly escaped disaster when the lighter broke loose from its towing launch.

Though plantation labor was in short supply, everyone turned to, to get the plants set out promptly. Within five days of their arrival, they were all planted in the nurseries of the Plant Quarantine Station. Few of the seeds or crated rhizomes had survived the trip, but the still alive growing plants took root promptly and throve in their new home. Eight months later, when he was convinced these plantings were really free from disease, the plantation manager had them transferred to Farm 9 of the Almirante Division of the United Fruit Company, where soil and moisture conditions should prove more favorable yet.

All the abacá plantings in all of Central America today can trace their ancestry back to that single acre on Farm 9, and through that to the plantations scattered along the Gulf of Davao in the Philippines, whose owners had been so generous in supplying healthy growing stock. That the plantations in Panama survived is due largely to the manager of Farm 9, Mr. J. H. Permar, plant breeder and horticulturist, who believed in Manila as a crop plant when practically everyone else was forgetting about it. With determination, he not only kept the plantations going but used his knowledge and experience to breed new, even more desirable strains of abacá. Incidentally, it was he who had been starting his days collecting seeds dropped by a lone Hevea tree that grew in the clearing near his house.

The bringing of abacá to Almirante had had a purpose beyond the possibility of starting a paying crop of fiber. For of all the known varieties of the plants that bear the name *Musa,* abacá is practically the only one that can produce the seed necessary for crossbreeding and the production of new varieties. By selection of plants and careful pollination of the flowers, the plant breeder tries to produce as offspring a third variety which may have some of the desirable traits of both parents. Without the formation of seeds, there is no possibility of achieving such results.

As the "Panama wilt" killed off more and more banana plantings, plant breeders thought to use the abacá, whose resistance to the disease had been demonstrated, to crossbreed with seedless bananas. If, by this means, resistant fruit-bearing plants could be attained, they planned to select rhizomes for relative seedlessness of the fruit and so, in the end, to combine in a single plant the two desired traits.

It was a good idea and a reasonable one but, as it turned out, disease resistance and salable fruit were not to be bred in one and the same plant. Abacá would not become the proud parent of generations of disease-free bananas. Then, as the depression years with their accompanying shortages of capital made the exploitation of a completely new crop impossible, interest in abacá plantations waned. The irreplaceable American abacá plantings might well have disappeared altogether had not Mr. Permar of Farm 9 seen to it that they were kept cleared from the ever encroaching jungle.

A year after the plants were set out in Almirante, they looked healthy and flourishing; eighteen years later they were still healthy. As, in 1927, they came to full maturity, Mr. Permar could start his work on hybridization. He developed seventy-four new combinations, some of them highly promising. Meanwhile, he was expanding the plantings with two new tracts of twenty-five acres each.

The time had come to settle once and for all the question whether American-grown abacá could produce fiber of a quality equal to the Philippine. A fiber-stripping machine was imported from the Islands and set up in Almirante. Leaves were cut, their stalks stripped of the fibrous sheaths, the fiber washed, dried, and shipped to the ropewalks of Boston. Only then might the value of the many years of effort by so many people be put to the crucial test. When the verdict came that the rope produced tested even somewhat better than that from Philippine sources, all obstacles to large-scale American abacá production should have disappeared.

One big obstacle still remained. Labor costs in the American tropics were higher than those in the Philippines and so American fiber would probably prove costlier, at the start at least. In depression years, this was a very important consideration. But the depression could not conceal from the United States Department of Agriculture and from cordage manufacturers that an American source of fiber was of utmost importance. In 1931 they sent a commission to Central America to study the abacá situation. The report was favorable but, for want of funds to develop the plantings, little was done about the situation for the next five years.

In 1936 they managed to scrape together enough money to pay for starting one thousand new acres and to purchase the needed stripping machinery. Great open sheds, roofed with corrugated iron sheets, were constructed to shelter the machines from the heavy rains while allowing free circulation of ai⁻. Cordage manufacturers encouraged the undertaking by agreeing to purchase the fiber output of these factories at prices prevailing in the world market at the time of sale.

With more and larger plantations now started, Mr. Permar found it possible to study methods of improving quality and yield of fiber. He found that pruning the weaker stalks from each clump encouraged the others to grow stronger and taller. Plantation workers were trained in these new techniques, and three years later another thousand acres could be set out and cared for. Meanwhile inventors set to work on a new and more efficient stripping machine which was manufactured and installed in 1939.

A crop that must be harvested in the warm, moist tropics presents problems that people living in temperate climes may have some difficulty in imagining. Where underbrush springs up as fast as sunlight is let in by the clearing away of the larger trees, roads in our northern sense are almost impossible to maintain. To be usable, such roads must not only be cleared and kept cleared, they must also be paved. Otherwise the ever deepening mud of the rainy season becomes churned into a practically bottomless, sticky mess. The jungle-wise planter uses narrow, shaded mule paths that lead to tramways whose cars run on narrow-gauge rails. The mules themselves keep their trails clear and the tracks may be cleared, as necessity arises, by machete-armed laborers riding the tramcars. As long as the two steel rails are unobstructed, neither undergrowth nor mud presents too serious a problem.

Like the bananas, abacá is harvested by these same machete-armed men who know how to sever each stalk with a single swing of the great blade. The leafy top is trimmed off, then the stalk is cut into six-foot lengths designed to fit each side of the mules' packsaddles. The mules, long accustomed to bearing bunches of bananas, one to each side of the saddle, wait patiently by, nibbling on leaves, then plod unhurriedly towards the tramlines or stripping shed. Behind, above ground, remain untidy piles of leaf tops and fruit stalks which, with incredible swiftness, insects and molds will reduce to nothing. Underground remains the still living network of abacá stems from which, with equally incredible swiftness, will rise a new plantation.

Even during the first eleven months of 1941, men still talked of the Central American abacá plantings as "experimental." On December 7, all that changed. In Washington the conference of growers, cordage manufacturers, and government experts decided upon the immediate planting, in Costa Rica and Panama, of ten thousand acres of abacá. Ten thousand acres! Where do you locate so many acres "immediately"? You cannot just grab it from other plantations. You've got to find undeveloped but suitable jungle. Do you buy it or rent it or just use your powers of diplomacy to persuade its owners to co-operate and, incidentally, enrich themselves?

Always, you've got to deal with local governments who have learned to be suspicious of foreign exploiters. When you have won their approval, you still have to find laborers to clear and plant the land — with other emergency projects actively competing for their services. You've got to provide housing and medical care and equip a plantation store to meet the everyday needs of men far removed from other sources of supply. You have to find suitable, experienced plantation managers. Trails, tramlines, and railroad spurs must be built so that your finished product can find ready access to the embarkation ports. You'll have to have equipment, of course, and of course an adequate supply of planting stock.

Fortunately, dwellers on remote tropical plantations where, even with roads, materials from the outside cannot be secured easily or cheaply or quickly have learned to improvise. This experience stood them in good stead while wartime shortages mounted. They made machetes from old steel rails, replaced torn fanbelts with weird substitutes made of rope, invented and built machines for drying and baling the finished fiber. For well drilling, to give the increased plantation population sufficient supplies of good water, old irrigation pipes were dug up. While in the United States and in Allied countries the stockpile of Philippine abacá dwindled alarmingly, abacá plantations were getting under way all over Central America.

You cannot, of course, hurry a plant's growth just because you may be in critical need of its product. You can, though, shave the two years needed for fullest maturity by a few months and, driven by dire necessity, harvest the immature crop. You'll get some fiber even if less than you should. More you cannot do. You just have to keep on planting and clearing underbrush and pruning and setting up machines — and waiting.

You could not even have got started in all this if there had not already been enough going abacá plantations to supply the needed rhizomes. Twenty-seven thousand tons of cuttings were dug in the experimental farms and shipped to plantations throughout Central America. These, in turn, shipped us some twenty million pounds of fiber during the war years. Not all this fiber arrived at its destination. Submarine sinkings reached far into the Caribbean and sent many a ship, loaded or destined to take on a load, to the bottom. Bales of fiber piled high on the docks. Railway congestion followed. Yet, somehow, enough got through.

This was because the plantations in Central America were extensive enough to cover the losses. By 1945, some twenty-nine thousand acres of abacá were growing in Honduras, Guatemala, Costa Rica, and Panama. That same year, the Philippine planters Charles Harvey and Henry Peabody were dying in a Japanese prison camp, while the products of their generosity of twenty years before were making an incalculable contribution to the final victory of their native land and of her allies.

VIII

The Big Leaf

IT MAY BE that plants have good reasons of their own for creating the special products by which men have come to know them. Still, it is hard to imagine what possible plant functions can be served by a bitter bark or a sticky juice or a nauseating oil. When it comes to the fiber of the abacá, some might be ready to suggest that the fiber was put there to give the leafstalks resistance to high winds. Undoubtedly, it is its ability to withstand winds that has helped the plant survive while weaker competitors were killed off. In any case, it's all a matter of conjecture and we scarcely expect to find a final answer.

We grow a little less cautious, though, when we talk of the stately carnauba palm that thrives in the incredibly dry coastal states of Brazil. Since we know that without the wax which coats its fronds, the tree could not survive, we're inclined to conclude that the wax was put there for just this purpose.

Whatever truth there may be in this, we do know that the climate there is cruel to most growing things. The clouds that have held the high Andean cinchona forests bound in cold, dripping fog moved on over the Amazon basin to pour forth their contents again and again in almost ceaseless downpours. Beyond the Araripe Mountains that divide the Amazon basin from the coastal states of Ceará and Piauí is a climate of violent contrasts.

If the skies still hold any moisture, it may be poured forth in a last tumultuous fling. Rivers rise swiftly and overflow their banks. As the waters run off, they shrink to nothing and the now brilliant sky blazes down upon a dry land. Ceará and Piauí are renowned for their prolonged droughts.

Loving his land, the Cearense will not leave until he knows that the only alternative for him and for his family is death. His thirsty cattle, hungry in their dry pastures, are already dead or dying. The earth is so dry that it is split by numberless deep cracks. The silence is like that of a graveyard from which even the insects have fled. So the Cearense gathers together his family and the most essential of his belongings and migrates to another state, there to wait impatiently until rains come again to Ceará and the merciless drought is broken.

In all the desolate scene, the one living green thing is the tall carnauba palm. It is the last thing he sees as he looks back longingly. He sees it still in his dreams as he waits out his exile and sings the hauntingly sad songs of homesickness which every other Brazilian recognizes as belonging to the dwellers in this unkind part of their country. The carnauba is the first thing to greet the returning exile, reminding him of home, promising him so many of the materials he needs for his simple existence.

How has this one tree managed to keep alive through the weeks and months of drought? Even were the roots strong enough and deep enough to reach some hidden and unsuspected source of water, the searingly hot winds should have burned the tops. Most other trees would have died long since. But other trees have no means to meet such crises. Their leaves have no special way of holding inside the life-giving water. The carnauba is prepared. Even in ordinary years, it protects the undersides of its fronds with a coating of wax that slows evaporation. Precious moisture is kept inside the leaves. When extra-long periods of drought come, the palm is ready. It builds up an extra-thick coating and, beautiful and indestructible, laughs at death.

When the Cearense returns — and the true Cearense always does — the palm is there, beckoning in welcome, promising to repay some of the bitter losses. He will harvest the largest fronds, using a sort of pruning shears attached to the end of a long pole. Then he lays the fronds out in the hot sun, which in the space of a few days will so have dried them that much of the wax separates in light, snowy white flakes. The remainder of the wax is removed by beating the fronds. Melted and molded, this crude product is ready for further purification or for shipment, as it is, to lands beyond the sea. It may end up in carbon paper or in furniture and floor waxes or colored and shaped into an infinite variety of decorative articles.

Cleaned of wax, the fronds serve many purposes. They may be woven into hats or fashioned into hammocks which, in tropical lands, are frequently preferred to beds. Or the Cearense may use the fronds to make fish nets, for much of his livelihood still comes from the sea. None of these uses interferes with the yield of wax. But when the tree is cut, as often it may be, for telephone poles or to provide for bridges the hard structural timbers which are especially resistant to salt water damage, full-grown trees are permanently destroyed. And when the green terminal bud is cut for salad and the young green fronds used for cattle fodder, future trees are also destroyed. As a result, the supply of carnauba wax is frequently insufficient to meet the world's demands.

What can be done about such shortages? The obvious answer would be to grow more palms — to set them out systematically in large, well-tended plantations. It could be done. But how can a man bring himself to invest so much time and work and money in a crop that must be eight or ten years away? In those years while the palms are coming to maturity, death may several times tread closely on the Cearense's heels. In a climate like that of Ceará, any long-term project of carnauba plantations needs financing by government agencies or by corporations that can afford to spend in the present and take their profits in the future. To start plantations elsewhere means all that and more: the finding of accessible areas with the kind of climate that, we may be thankful, is not too common on our globe.

When wax shortages faced us during World War II, it was already too late to consider starting carnauba plantations. The alternative was to seek for other wax-producing plants. Waxes, like coagulable juices and sweet saps, are produced by many different kinds of plants for many different plant reasons: to keep water in, as with the carnauba, or to keep water out, as with some plants of the tropical rainforest. The problem was not just to find another wax-producing plant — that would have been quite easy. It was necessary to find a quite common plant that formed lots of easily removable wax and did not grow too skimpily in too remote areas.

As soon as people recognized this need, others began looking busily around for such a plant. Word presently leaked out from somewhere in the Amazon basin that a giant-leaved plant was growing there that just might fill the bill. Manufacturers of products that required wax and wax chemists listened attentively. They knew, of course, the rumor might be false. If the rumor turned out to be true, the wax might not be of usable quality. Perhaps they could not again locate the plant or, if they did locate it, they might find it in too remote spots or in too small quantity to meet the steadily increasing demands. On the other hand, as matters stood, any lead was worth following.

It had long been known that natives of the region used large leaves as raincoats or as waterproof wrappings for the loads they carried. Some such leaves formed shelter over men and cargoes in the dugout canoes that plied the rivers and streams of that area. Both Alexander von Humboldt and Henry Wickham had such roofing over their own *toldas* — canoes. What kind of waterproofing did such leaves have? Was it usable wax and could there be enough of it for profitable exploitation? This would mean profit not alone for the foreigners who bought it but for the jungle dwellers themselves, the river boats that might transport it, and the government, which could fix an export duty if it chose to do so.

News of this "cauassú" — the big-leaved plant — worked its way down the river to Belém de Pará. In due time it was relayed to the Brazilian Government Trade Bureau offices in New York, which informed an interested wax chemist, Nelson Knaggs. That was all the clue — the name "cauassú," which meant "big leaf," and a statement that it had been found along the Tocantins River, which is a tributary of the Amazon. The quest could turn out like the traditional hunt for a needle in a haystack, but the need was so great that the chemist decided that even a dim cold trail should be followed.

Those were the years when every available professional botanist was employed in the search for exploitable wild stands of Cinchona and Hevea. There were no professional plant hunters to spare for a search for any less vital material like wax. So the chemist undertook it himself. Armed with every imaginable chemical — from halozone for purifying water to quinine and atabrine for malaria and antivenin for snakebites — that he thought might reduce the much talked about hazards of jungle travel, he set forth for Belém de Pará and the offices of the Commercial Association there.

The secretary of the Association was most helpful. Yes, they had leaves of this cauassú in their plant collections — from the Tocantins River, as you know, Senhor. Unfortunately now in the dry season there would not be sufficient depth of water to permit of steamboat passage. In a few months, though, it would again be deep enough to permit a steamboat to pass. There was nothing to be done about it. However, if the Senhor wished to learn more about the plant in the meantime, there was in Belém a man who knew that part of the country like the palm of his hand — knew the Indians who lived there. Would the Senhor care to talk with him?

So Arqueminis Prestes was called in — a slight, frail-looking man in his middle fifties. The *Norteamericano,* who had been hoping for a guide and companion in his upriver journey, was at first disappointed. How could so frail a man survive those anticipated risks of jungle life? It wouldn't be fair to ask his help in that way. Yet a guide and interpreter would be needed . . .

Senhor Prestes' eyes lighted with enthusiasm as he began to talk about his favorite subject. "We have right here in Belém," he exclaimed eagerly, "a French botanist named Paul LeCointe. For years he has been making a great study of the plants of our land. Here is his book. And here — see — he has written about our cauassú . . ."

There, indeed, it was printed: *"Calathea lutea,* Family Marantaceae, popular name cauassú." So, after all, it already had a botanical name and a place in a botanical family not too far from the banana and abacá! A detailed botanical description followed; then, according to botanical tradition, a list of localities where the plant had been found. Banks of the Amazon, it said, and of rivers emptying into it — especially abundant near a town called Gurupá.

A definite locality at last! A place that might be pinpointed upon a sufficiently large and detailed map of the Amazon! Best of all, an Amazon port known to captains of the steamboats that plied the river, even if it was so small a port that most boats passed it by!

The would-be travelers made inquiries and found that on the following day a boat would be leaving Belém for a month's journey upriver to the port of Iquitos in Peru. Gurupá was not on its itinerary. However, the captain, who had to make frequent stops to load firewood for the never satisfied furnaces, could be persuaded to add yet another brief stop to his list. Two paying passengers with luggage for Gurupá! It might be managed, Senhor!

So the Norteamericano and Senhor Prestes hurriedly assembled their baggage and boarded the old *Fortaleza* the next morning. In her far distant youth the *Fortaleza* may well have been the last word in river liner luxury, but there had been many later words. Now, heavily loaded with passengers, their baggage, and their livestock which lowed and clucked and quacked and grunted noisily, she made her slow and wheezy way upstream.

The passengers, most of them headed for remote, isolated settlements where new faces would be rare and most of the old topics of conversation long since used up, found the foreigner in their midst a wonderful conversation piece. Where was he going? Not Gurupá, Senhor, when there are so many bigger and more attractive towns much nearer! But why? To collect plants? They shook their heads in friendly disbelief and told one another that all foreigners were a little crazy. The foreigner watched and listened, enjoying every moment of this close and cordial association with the people of another land. The days of river travel passed happily and unhurriedly.

No one in Gurupá was expecting the *Fortaleza* to call there, but, knowing the unpredictableness of steamers, the inhabitants always were more or less prepared for just such an emergency. The anchor had not touched the surface of the water before canoes shot out from shore. Loaded with fruit and fish and eggs to sell to the steamer and its passengers, they did a lively business for the few moments it took to arrange for one of them to take the passengers and their baggage to the shore. The *Fortaleza* tooted a last farewell, drew in its anchor, and was moving away before those passengers were able to set foot on shore. They were now committed to the town, to its inhabitants, and to the surrounding jungle until such a time as another steamer, bound downriver for Belém, might make Gurupá a port of call.

One remote tropical American village is not too unlike another, especially in those ways that distinguish it from villages of temperate climates. Houses, whose only requirements are to grant their owners occasional privacy and frequent protection from the violence of tropical downpours, are made of materials easily and cheaply available on the spot. Import duties, river freight charges, and middlemen's profits make any other kind of construction far too costly.

Upright timbers may be cut in the forest nearby, sharpened at one end, and driven into the ground. Or the frame may be more elaborately and skillfully put together. Walls will probably be of closely set poles — possibly bamboo — or of adobe bricks fashioned from the never lacking mud. Floors may be of hard-packed, clean-swept earth, and roofs of overhanging thatch that sheds most of the rain while permitting most of the smoke from the cookfires to find its way out. Windows may boast shutters, but rarely useless, fragile, and expensive glass panes. If the owner is sufficiently enlightened and sufficiently prosperous, there will be window and door screens — in which case the thatched roof will have been replaced by sheets of corrugated metal which reverberate thunderously when the rains beat upon them.

The primitive construction of such homes may mislead the foreigner into thinking all the inhabitants equally primitive. This may or may not be the case, for homes in such climes do

not have to serve the same functions as homes in more northern areas. Snow, cold, and ice are never a hazard there.
Ventilation is highly important, as also is good insulation from
sun and rain. So the light walls of poles or the heavy walls of
adobe are really the best for the climate. And that romantic-
looking thatch is just what is needed to permit ventilation
while giving protection from the direct rays of the sun or from
wind-driven rains. A simple home, easily built, easily replaced
when fungi or insects invade and destroy, serves all purposes
best.

The risks of life in such a settlement are a commonplace
and the life itself often seems monotonous. A stranger in town,
as on the steamer, brings excitement and interest. If the
stranger happens to come from that fascinating, distant land
which — if you can believe it, Senhor — is even farther away
than Rio, the village is set on its ear. Can he talk a civilized
tongue? Will he eat native dishes without complaining? Is he
safe to have around or will he turn out to be one of those
gangsters in which his country is known to abound? Uncon-
cealed curiosity — sometimes worried, sometimes touching,
usually friendly, frequently embarrassing — follows the traveler from the moment he sets foot in a village like Gurupá.

Swift inspection of Senhor Knaggs — plus, possibly, Senhor
Prestes' diplomatic assurances — promptly convinced the inhabitants of Gurupá that their visitor was a respectable gentleman. The house of the chief official was put at the Norteamericano's service. Since, however, it was a bachelor's estab-
lishment, meals would have to be secured elsewhere — in this
case at the home of the chief of police. The police chief, who
had formerly lived in Belém, knew his house and fare to be
poor by outside standards, yet he generously welcomed his
guests. Sleeping or eating, the strangers in town found them-

selves and their every action watched with intense interest.

With the acute war shortages of rubber, the gathering of wild rubber had again become highly profitable. Seringueiros came and went in Gurupá as in many another river port up and down the Amazon. A month along the forest trails and before his latex smoking fires; then a visit to the port to sell his rubber or to exchange it for trade goods such as a gay length of printed calico for his wife or a beautiful long sharp knife — a *terçado* — manufactured in Collinsville, Connecticut, for himself.

As they stood in the open store, lovingly fingering the display of terçados, carefully making sure that each bore the little black label that would assure the illiterate that it was of the manufacture they desired, they relaxed and found the words they had used little in their solitary travels to chat with the strangers.

When these strangers asked, "And have you, perhaps, come upon a plant called 'cauassú'?" they would smile tolerantly, take their time in anwering while they looked the Norteamericano over.

"But, of course, Senhor! We use it to wrap our fish and mandioca, to keep them dry. The biggest leaves cover our toldas. Even an idiot would know the cauassú, Senhor."

"Then you could tell me where I might find it growing?"

"Why not, Senhor? It is everywhere — along the river, in the forest — everywhere. It grows up again as fast as you can cut it. Even a blind man could find the cauassú."

A fast-growing plant! All along the rivers! Good news, indeed!

So they hired two dugout canoes and their boatmen and, with the police chief added to their party, set out for the Arinhoa River, which empties into the Amazon not far from

Gurupá. The Arinhoa, a small, narrow river, shone darkly under the arches of trees whose soaring branches met and mingled above its waters. All along its banks, lush vegetation grew so thickly that there seemed to be no single spot where a man might set his foot.

And there, presently, they saw the cauassú. Growing, like its second cousin the banana, in clumps of green stems that shot up to a height of perhaps fifteen feet, topped with great elliptical leaves, possibly three feet long, it crowded to the very edge of the water. So they hacked away from the canoes until they had cleared a foothold on the shore and could make as large a collection of the big leaves as their canoes could carry.

Sure enough, there was the telltale whitish coating on the underside of the leaves! Was it wax? The Norteamericano reached for his box of matches, struck one, and held it close to the leaf. The flame sputtered a bit; then, slowly, the area near the flame grew smooth and shiny. So it was something that melted easily, this white coating on the underside of the leaves! Probably it was wax and probably plenty of it to justify this expedition to Gurupá. Of course only careful laboratory tests could give the final answer as to what it really was. And even if each leaf yielded less than a carnauba frond, it promised much to a wax-hungry world — this plant that you could cut so easily one year and find replaced the next.

The excited men bore their canoefuls of great leaves back to Gurupá. In a wide, sunny spot, the leaves were spread out to dry. One important question would soon be answered: Might the wax be easily separated from the leaves? Five days were required to complete the drying of the carnauba fronds — days in which some of the feather-light wax scales might blow away and be lost. Would the cauassú require more or less? The carnauba's very existence, of course, depended upon its ability to hold on to its wax in the driest seasons. What about the cauassú, which grew in wet jungles? As it turned out, two and a half hours sufficed to separate half the wax in flakes. The remainder was easy to scrape off. The future of cauassú wax began to look very bright.

There were yet two questions to be answered. How generally throughout the jungles did the cauassú grow? And might there be other wax-bearing plants in that jungle that might repay exploitation? So the little party made more elaborate plans for a prolonged camping trip up the Arinhoa River. All Gurupá was excited at the thought of a possible new source of income growing so close at hand. The Brazilians in the camping party were especially excited because the *patron* had promised his fine hunting knife as a prize to the first man who should discover a new wax-bearing plant. A beautiful imported knife like that was more to be desired than money.

So, as again and again they drew their toldas to the shore, the men leaped out eagerly, reached for their boxes of matches, and began running the flickering match flames up and down every leaf in sight. While daylight lasted and into the swift tropic twilight they continued their tests until the jungle seemed to have been invaded by a swarm of large fireflies. Several new wax-producing plants came to light, the first being found by José, the police chief of Gurupá.

Each night, as darkness settled about them, the men had to clear a small space in the jungle, throw up crude palm-thatched shelters, and hang their sleeping hammocks under these. They drifted off to sleep amid the sounds and smells of the jungle: the high-pitched chorus of tree frogs, the bass grunt of a hunting tapir, the heavy, moisture-laden odors of lush vegetation, alive or disintegrating in decay.

The jungle also had its dangers, seen and unseen, few of them of the kind to be warded off with the chemicals the Nortcamericano had brought with him. For most of the snakes seemed far more afraid of the men than the men were of them. Bird-size scorpions were more of a menace. *Tigre* (jaguar) tracks reminded them of the risks of meeting tigres and made them cautious even if they never encountered a tigre in the flesh.

The most formidable threats came from the plants themselves. A jungle tree must play host to numberless uninvited guests that sap its strength and remain attached to it as long as it stands. The least of these, the mosses and lichens, grow on the outside of its bark. Birds or winds drop orchid and wild pineapple seeds into the moist crotches between the spreading branches and there they grow luxuriant and heavy. Creepers and lianas — the "bush-ropes" once described by Henry Wickham — find their way up the trunk and out along the branches, from which they may send down fine rope-like roots to the ground below. Lush aroid leaves clothe the trunk. Then, perhaps, a strangler fig runs up the trunk, encircling it completely, until it is choked to death. Yet it does not fall, for it cannot; the intricate network of woody vines and creepers binds it to its neighbors in one great whole.

Eventually decay sets in and the dead giant is invaded by termites and wood-boring insects and fungi which, in the moist heat of the tropics, soon destroy it. Still the living shell stands and grows in lushness and weight with each passing rainy season. In the end, though, there comes a time when too many trees have thus died or too much weight has been added. A trifle more weight — an extra-heavy rain or a playful tribe of monkeys — becomes that last straw. The trees start to quake, at first gently, then with increasing violence; cracking and tearing sounds are heard — and anyone who knows what's what in the jungle runs for dear life.

Such a moment came to the wax-hunting party from Gurupá. The Brazilians looked up into the trees, saw the ominous quaking, and shouted urgently to their foreign companion to run. He did, wondering what might be in pursuit. Then, when he was barely beyond its reach, came the terrifying roaring and crashing that brought a great section of jungle — the living with the dead — to the earth in a jumbled mass.

It was an almost invisible plant that brought the expedition to an end. One morning, after a night of misery, the Norteamericano woke up to find his arms and legs covered with a mass of tiny red and white blisters that itched and burned intolerably. It seemed to him at that moment that he had sought far enough and that nothing more he might hope to find could lessen his wretchedness. So he called his companions to him and suggested a return to Gurupá. "These accursed insects!" he exploded.

"Those are no insect bites, Senhor," Arqueminis Prestes assured him gently.

"Then what can it be?"

"A little plant we call 'juiquiri.' See — here it is. The edges of the leaves have tiny spines. These got into your skin — "

"But Arqueminis," exclaimed the sufferer, "you must be mistaken. Yesterday you yourself walked barefoot through just such plants. Why is it you have no such blisters?"

"*Quem sabe,* Senhor?" Arqueminis replied with a shrug of his shoulders. "It may be that it is because God is a Brazilian."

Which, also, may be a good way of accounting for the success of the expedition up the Arinhoa River. It had revealed several new wax-bearing plants, some with definite plantation possibilities.

IX

Life from
the Flying Death

WHEN THE SPANISH CONQUISTADORES overran the great
empire of the Incas and won for themselves the Incas' fabulous
treasures, they found it hard not to believe that still greater
treasures were kept hidden from them. After the manner of
most European adventurers, whatever their homelands or century, the Spanish dreamed of wealth only in terms of gold or

of easily salable articles of great value. They wanted no second glance on the natural resources within their reach — resources which would eventually prove more valuable than gold because they were self-renewing.

To the natives of South America, on the other hand, gold was just a bright, untarnishing metal for the adornment of their persons or of the temples of the sun god whom they worshiped. They saw the conquistadores as greedy, grasping, undesirable strangers and used appropriate methods to rid themselves of the aliens. Gold, if anything, should be able to draw them off.

Somewhere, these natives admitted when questioned, far in the depths of the continent, was indeed a city greater than any yet found, a city shining with gold. "El Dorado!" the Spanish exclaimed, as the greediest hastened to move on to get there first. Men usually believe what they wish to believe; so, though there was nothing in the quest to encourage them, they continued in search of El Dorado, moving on and on looking for a glorious city which they would never find, while they ignored the greater green wealth they could reach out and touch.

Other lands were bound to hear rumors of El Dorado. Since England was then at war with Spain, English adventurers did not hesitate to organize their own expeditions to search for the prize within the Spanish overseas dominions. To snatch these treasures out from under the very nose of Spain could be doubly rewarding, at one and the same time enriching themselves and humiliating their enemies.

In 1617 Sir Walter Raleigh, encouraged by King James I of England, set out to find the city. This was the same gallant Raleigh who had, as a young man, made legend by throwing his cloak across a mud puddle so that his queen, Elizabeth I, need not soil her royal feet. For her he had made his first voyage to Guiana, an adventure he described in a book entitled *The Discoverie of the Large and Bewtiful Empire of Guiana Performed in the Year 1595.*

Older, soberer after some years as a prisoner in the Tower, Raleigh still believed in 1617 that he could locate El Dorado in this Empire of Guiana. Of course he failed. He brought home no wealth either he or his sovereign had the imagination to value. In Guiana he left the body of his son Walter, slain in a fight with the Spanish. On his return home, his vacillating king had him executed in order to appease the angry Spanish. The only enduring profit to come out of Sir Walter's voyages of exploration would be his recorded accounts of the strange new lands and peoples he had visited.

"These are valiant, or rather desperate people," he wrote of the natives he encountered during his ascent of the Orinoco River, "and have the most strong poyson on their arrowes, and most dangerous to all nations; of which poyson I will speak somewhat, being a digression not unnecessary. There was nothing of which I was more curious than to find out the true remedie of these poysoned arrowes; For, beside the mortalitie of the wound they make, the partie indureth the most insufferable torments in the wound. . . . And it is more strange to know that in all this time there never was Spaniard, either by gift or torment, that could attain to the true knowledge of the cure, although that they have martured and put to invented torture I know not how many of them. But every one of these Indians know it not, no, not one among thousands; but their soothsayers and priestes who do conceal it, and only teach it but from father to son."

This, one of the first accounts of the flying death written by an Englishman, shows clearly how Sir Walter, the soldier, was fascinated by the thought of it. A substance that could make the slightest scratch fatal could render worse than useless heavy armor like that he and his men — and the Spaniards, too — bore so wearily through the tropical heat of Guiana. The frail, slender, poison-tipped arrows, soundlessly flying through jungle fastnesses, filled him with a horror that made him exaggerate the torment of the death they inflicted. Centuries later, it would appear that the real horror was in the painless suffocation induced by the arrow poison that has borne many names — "urare," "woorali," "curare," among them.

The soldier in Sir Walter must have made him consider the value of such poison applied to his own arms. Yet without knowledge of an antidote, it would prove too risky. Otherwise it might well have become the great secret weapon of the seventeenth century — that is, if it were not also so extremely hard to get and the plants of which it was compounded not even to be guessed at.

The "soothsayers" — the witch doctors of the jungle tribes which the Spanish called *"brujos"* — guarded their secrets well. They couldn't care less if the annoying outsiders used the curare upon each other. But the brujos cared a great deal about holding on to their own personal power and they knew that their knowledge of drugs and poisons and the elaborate rituals of magic which surrounded them were what kept their own power and influence among their tribesmen. Naturally they agreed wholeheartedly with the ancient tribal tradition that decreed that only with other witch doctors might such priceless knowledge be shared.

Only with other witch doctors! Throughout the centuries, outsiders have again and again sought for the secret and have been ready to pay well. Yet today, when purified and standardized curare is available in sterile ampules to physicians and surgeons of the outside world, that rule of sharing still holds.

In all the intervening years, there are only three or four records of any native of the jungles sharing with uninitiated brujos even part of the secret of curare preparation.

One of these outsiders was an Englishman named Edward Bancroft, who in 1769 gave a list of the ingredients he had been told went into arrow poison: six parts of the root of "Woorara," two parts of the bark of "Warracobba coura," one part each of "Couranapi, Baketi, and Hatchybaly." But what plants were designated by these names, no one knew. Like the "kalaw," they might turn out to be anything to any man. Probably the Indians had no intention of revealing which they were.

Some thirty-five years later, the naturalist Alexander von Humboldt — the same von Humboldt whose route up the Orinoco and down the Rio Negro Henry Wickham would retrace — gave an eyewitness account of the preparation of curare as seen in the town of Esmeralda in "Guiana": "We were fortunate enough to find an old Indian less drunk than the others and who was occupied with the preparation of curare poison from the freshly collected plants. This was the local chemist. . . . He had the impassive air and pedantic tone formerly found in the European pharmacist.

" 'I know,' said he, 'that the whites have the secret for making soap and this black powder which if it misses has a fault of making a loud noise which scares away the animal. Curare which we prepare is far superior to that which you make over there, beyond the seas. It is the juice of a plant which kills quietly without one knowing whence the blow came.' "

Obviously sophisticated beyond the usual practitioner of witchcraft, this curare maker let von Humboldt watch him prepare the poison brew and gave him a sample of the product. Yet von Humboldt failed to learn what plants went into the brew, where they were collected, and just how to repeat the process.

Some thirty years later, in the 1830's, the brothers Robert and Richard Schomburgk made the next recorded observations of curare preparation. Born in Prussia, these brother botanists spent most of their lives in England and in British overseas territory. Robert was finally knighted for his services to the land of his adoption.

"After I had engaged some guides," Robert wrote of his first attempts in Guiana to discover the plant source of curare, "I started in the morning of the 25th of December, in search of the mysterious plant. Our way led first to the south, over pathless savanahs [plains], until we met with a place in the Rupununi [River] where we could ford it. . . .

"At last, after we had walked more than five miles . . . the ascent commenced. It was by no means an easy matter; the the path, Indian-like, quite narrow, led over fallen trees, between boulders of granite, and was often so steep that we had to use hands and feet. . . .

"At three o'clock in the afternoon, after a most fatiguing march of eight hours and a half, we reached a few huts on Mount Mamesua, inhabited by Wapisianas, and learned from our host Oronappi, an old acquaintance, whom we had met a few weeks ago in the valley, that he himself knew how to prepare the poison, and that he would willingly accompany our guide and bring the plant for our inspection.

"This proposal did not agree with my plans. I was anxious to see the plant in its native growth, and when we gave him to understand that it was our intention to accompany him, he attempted by signs to make us desist from going with him. He told us that the path was very bad, and that it was so far that we could not reach the place till afternoon, and that we would have to sleep on the road; he repeated the same story in the morning, and as he observed that we were determined to insist on our first plan, he made a sour face and did not speak for a length of time. Whether he thought that we were not able to stand the fatigues, or whether he wished us not to learn the place where the plant grew, I know not; . . . the path was wretched; all traces of it were frequently lost, and an Indian only could have guided us; and he directed his course mostly by broken branches, or marks cut in the trees, sometimes standing still for a few moments to consider in which direction to turn.

"Our path was over 'hill and dale.' . . . It became every moment wilder: we had to cross several mountain-streams, which flowed in deep beds . . . underbrush became scarce; it appeared as if Nature here delighted only in gigantic forms . . . as we arrived at a stream that ran rapidly over sloping ground, our guides stopped, and pointing to a ligneous twiner which wound itself snakelike from tree to tree, they called out 'Urari', the name of the plant in the tongue of our guides.

"My wish was thus realized; and the plant which Baron de Humboldt was prevented from seeing, I now saw before me."

The plant was not in flower — a detail usually necessary to determine with accuracy the botanical relationships of plants. "Though I did not find the plant in flower," he wrote, "it was bearing fruit and their inspection assured me that as von Humboldt suspected, the plant belongs to the genus *Strychnos*." Though he saw the plant, he had no opportunity at all of seeing how the poison was prepared from it.

Disappointed in this outcome of the exciting and dangerous quest, Robert Schomburgk determined to try again later. On another expedition into the interior of Guiana he "found opportunity to revisit the regions which, in consequence of the arrow poison, had been previously of interest to me. . . . During our stay in Pirara, a Macusi village on the classical site of Raleigh and Keymis' El Dorado, I ascertained that an Indian lived in the vicinity, who was far-famed for the preparation of Urari poison. I induced him by presents of some consideration to prepare it in my presence, and he promised to do so."

Always with the hope of being able to collect the plants in flower, Schomburgk accompanied this Indian, too, in search for the ingredients of the "Urari" poison. Again they encountered no flowers. However, three baskets were filled with the necessary materials and brought back to the village.

Preparation of the poison could not be begun immediately, for the jungle chemist knew it could turn out to be worthless unless he fasted rigidly for several days before undertaking it. Meanwhile an influential Macusi chief arrived on the scene and persuaded the poison maker to retract his promise. Fortunately for Schomburgk, as he wrote, "The bark was in my keeping, and as I had paid for it, I considered myself to have a full right to it; and although he demanded it back, it was my turn to refuse him . . . and with the pure bark in my possession, we departed."

A brave man to turn his back on an angry Indian whose silent arrows were tipped with curare, who knew how to place those arrows in his long, slim, reed-lined blowgun, who knew how to aim that blowgun and how to fill his lungs and empty them so that the force of his breath would drive the arrow straight to its mark. Fortunately for Schomburgk, it was animals, not men, that Indians were accustomed to slaying with their arrows. The foreigner, they undoubtedly told themselves, was hardly worth the trouble of ambushing and thrusting through with spears. For, since he could not know the solemn Indian rituals needed for the preparation of "Urari," the barks he bore away with him could serve him no useful purpose.

The Indians would never know that in a safely distant spot, the stranger would extract the bark with water, boil the extract to concentrate it, and test the product upon chickens who died in less than half an hour in a manner typical of death by arrow poison. Definitely weaker than the usual jungle-made curare, this preparation convinced Schomburgk that he really had in his hands one source, at least, of the true arrow poison.

It was the brother, Richard Schomburgk, who in the 1840's would have the privilege of being perhaps the first white man to view the whole process of curare preparation. And while he could not manage to ascertain the botanical names of all plants, he recorded the ones he could determine and the Indian names for the others, together with the weight of each component that went into the brew. The account, published in 1879 when he was director of the Botanical Garden in Adelaide, Australia, gives his observations in detail: "At last my long cherished wish to witness the preparation of *urari,* of which many fables had been told (as there always will be about anything enveloped in a certain mystery), was to be fulfilled, and I found the process, except a few unimportant ceremonies, as simple as possible."

When he examined the collected ingredients, he was told that they grew "far, far away in the mountains; it would take him five days to get there." The poison maker arranged with due ceremony the deep earthenware pot for extracting the curare and the shallow vessels for evaporating the brew. Then he pounded the various ingredients to pulp in a wooden mortar.

"The *urari* maker, after having arranged everything, built a hearth with three stones and laid the wood ready to light the fire though there was a large fire burning close by us, but which was of no use, being lighted by profane hands. Neither dare he use any water except that brought in the pot to be used for the operation; in fact, no other implement could be used but such as has been made by the cook; neither would he have assistance from any of the inhabitants. Any transgression of the sacred rules would nullify the operation of the poison. . . . As soon as the water began to boil the Indian added at certain intervals a handful of the other ingredients except the Muramu root. In doing so, he bent his head over the pot, strongly blowing into the mixture, which he said afterwards was adding considerably to the strength of the poison. . . .

"Within the next twenty-four hours, the old man left the fire only for one moment, keeping the mixture at an equal heat."

In that time, the mixture had become somewhat concentrated. The old man then filtered it and set it out in the flat pots for the sun's heat to accomplish further evaporation. Finally he added the Muramu root which gave it the consistency of heavy molasses. By the third day, the poison was ready for testing on animals. Cold-blooded animals — lizards — were used for this because with them the test would be more sensitive. If a lizard died in one minute — as it did — then warm-blooded animals would be killed in half the time.

Thus, though only in part, was the mystery of arrow poison cleared up. The pursuit of the poison was made no easier by the fact that over a wide area of South America, Indians use poisons on their arrows and each group of Indians may have its own secret formula. All they cared about a poison was that it kill quickly without making the slaughtered game unfit to eat. The plant constituents of several samples of such poisons from different tribes might be practically identical or might vary considerably. No one would be sure until the plants had been collected and thoroughly studied by competent botanists. Yet, so far, in a hundred years of trying, no one had managed to identify all the ingredients of just one sample of curare.

Meanwhile the explorers of the laboratory had become actively interested in the mysterious substance. Though chemists of the 1850's were fascinated by the question of the chemical identity of curare, their science had not reached the stage of development which would enable them to isolate and study the pure alkaloids that give curare its special character. Today's chemists not only know how to determine the percentage composition of such alkaloids in terms of carbon, hydrogen, oxygen, and nitrogen, they can actually draw a diagram of each molecule, placing the atoms in a definite, if incredibly intricate, pattern.

Biologists did not have to know this chemical structure to study the physiological effects of the molasses-like material put up in crude jungle containers such as calabashes or sections of hollow bamboo stems. How, these scientists asked, did curare kill? What functions of that intricate mechanism which is the human body does curare so interfere with that life must cease? Bit by bit, they narrowed the possibilities. Death resulted from complete muscular relaxation which brought vital functions like breathing to an end. Was the action of the drug directly upon muscle tissues or on the nerves which supplied impulses to the muscles? That question they determined to answer in the only way men could: by seeing what curare did to animals.

In 1814 an Englishman named Charles Waterton, who had

traveled widely in Guiana and had brought home a gourd of the "real, original Wourali-poison," obtained directly from Indians there, tested the product upon several asses.

"Several experiments were made with the wourali poison," he wrote. "A she-ass received the wourali poison in the shoulder and died apparently in ten minutes. An incision was then made in its windpipe and through it the lungs were regularly inflated for two hours with a pair of bellows. Suspended animation returned. The ass held up her head and looked around; but the inflating being discontinued, she sunk once more in apparent death. The artificial breathing was immediately recommenced, and continued without intermission for two hours. This saved the ass from final dissolution; she rose up, and walked about; she seemed neither in agitation nor pain. The wound, through which the poison entered, was healed without difficulty. . . . She looked lean and sickly for above a year, but began to mend the spring after, and by summer became fat and frisky.

"The kind hearted reader will rejoice on learning that Earl Percy, pitying her misfortunes, sent her down from London to Walton Hall, near Wakefield. There she goes by the name of Wouralia. Wouralia shall be sheltered from the wintry storm; and when summer comes she shall feed in the finest pasture. No burden shall be placed upon her and she shall end her days in peace."

Wouralia did end her days happily in fine pastures nearly twenty-five years later, a footnote records. Perhaps the other asses in the pasture, incapable of understanding her great contributions to science, envied her her favored position. Unknowing and unasked, she had risked her life to show men how curare acts and, incidentally, to demonstrate that if respiration be maintained, the effects of the poison may pass off and the victims may survive.

When the true nature of these effects became evident, it occurred to physicians that here might be a means of counteracting the terrible muscle spasms that make tetanus infections (lockjaw) so painful and so fatal. As early as 1811, a Dr. Brodie of England suggested this application. Yet it was not until 1858, long after Wouralia had gone to her grave, that, after testing curare on horses infected with tetanus, it was tried upon similarly infected humans. Though not always effective, curare was yet effective enough to offer the first real hope of saving the otherwise doomed victims of tetanus.

Today, a century later, you may still find in medical journals case histories of the treatment of "severe systemic tetanus" by means of the now purified curare alkaloid. This same alkaloid is also used in the treatment of spastic paralysis, in shock therapy to lessen the intensity of the bone-breaking spasms which so often accompany it, and in anesthesia. Combined with a noninflammable, inhaled anesthetic like nitrous oxide, it can give a satisfactory anesthesia for throat surgery where inflammable mixtures constitute a real danger. The cautery so often required in such operations can supply the spark to ignite them. What future lifesaving purposes our modern standardized curare may serve, we cannot even guess.

We do know, though, that most of the effects of curare upon the muscles of human beings were known to European physicians over a century ago. Many of the drug's present uses had been thought of and tried and the results found sufficiently successful to encourage further tests. Moreover, Richard Schomburgk had already seen and tentatively identified some of the important plants that went into the poison maker's brew.

So why, you well may ask, haven't such drugs been in general medical use until recent years?

Richard Schomburgk, remember, saw only a few specimens of the plants growing many days' rough journey far into the jungles in the interior of South America. Tropical jungles may not be more impenetrable than some northern forests but they differ in one very important aspect. They are a mingling of trees of a great many different kinds — a jumble where you may have to tramp many difficult miles to find two identical plants. Besides, since you are on the forest floor, and flowers and fruit and even leaves are borne far, far above where there is sunlight, you may find yourself forced to make identification from stem and bark alone. It takes an expert botanist to detect significant differences where, to the average person, one woody vine out of the thousands that drape themselves from tree to tree looks very much like another. The curare-producing plant is such a vine.

Most important of all, one vine or ten or even a hundred cannot produce enough of the alkaloid to enable men to launch a new and dangerously potent drug upon the market. The dark sticky messes that the Indians smear upon their arrow tips will not do. If you are going to use it upon people instead of lizards or asses or horses, or even guinea pigs, you have to be pretty sure just what you have and know how much makes a dose. Purified and standardized — any drug in common use must be that.

Soon we find ourselves running in circles. Curare must be purified before it can be given adequate physiologic testing, yet you cannot be sure of its purity until it has been tested. The process of purification and standardization has many pitfalls. Physiologic testing requires large amounts of the pure drug. Or should we say "drugs"? How do the various arrow

poisons differ? Which to try, where to get it (or them), how
to get it, how to make sure of a constant supply — all these
are questions that, in the course of the first hundred years,
never even approached solution. Do not forget that with
curare there could be no native lore to guide. Curare was
primarily a native poison, not a native remedy like quinine
or chaulmoogra oil.

Yet time was running out. As civilization has encroached,
the art of brewing arrow poisons has gradually disappeared.
To find witch doctors who still perform the ancient ritual of
poison making requires ever longer and more dangerous trips
into the untouched jungle. And this, in turn, demands a patient, courageous plant hunter who can talk the Indians'
languages, who understands their way of life and their curious
patterns of thought and so can earn their trust and respect.

The impulse to make an exhaustive study of native curares,
to plunge into the dark jungles in order to bring back large
amounts of curare from many different sources and to bring
also identifiable specimens of all the plants that went into such
brews, could never have come through an interest in curare's
death-dealing powers alone. It was a personal need for curare
as a drug — a realization that it might be the only one that
could bring relief from the spastic paralysis that had kept him
bedridden — which sent the plant hunter on his quest. Curare
might help, the physician said, if only enough of it was available and in some purified standardized form. It was something
the Indians used to poison their arrows, but it had remarkable
life-giving properties if used right.

Perhaps many another sufferer had heard those same not
very encouraging words. This time they fell on the ears of a
man who would be able to do something about it. Richard C.
Gill was the man's name and he was the owner of a ranch in

eastern Ecuador on the very edge of the wilderness whose rivers drain into the Amazon basin. The trail that passed his remote dwelling bore, like a river, a continuous current of humanity.

Out of the jungle came Indian visitors, curious to set eyes upon the strange white man and woman and the stranger house they had heard incredible tales about. Shyly, apologetically, they would approach the patron and ask permission to camp on his land. So he had a chance to talk with them and watch their manner of living even as they watched his. Gradually there grew up an odd friendship between the modern couple and these people of the Stone Age.

Then, one bright day, the patron's horse reared at the sight of a quivering leaf and the patron wrenched his back badly. Gradually a spastic paralysis overcame him and, as he lay in bed in his home in Washington, D.C., he asked himself bitterly if, ever again, he should see his Ecuadorian ranch, ride his horse, visit his Indian friends. The most skilled physicians could promise him nothing — nothing, that is, without a drug that couldn't be had. A dangerous drug if not properly handled; a powerful drug, as those who had handled it knew. There were interesting records in the medical literature. If there were enough of it available, and it was pure enough — But no use talking — it was a secret of the Indians of the jungles of the Amazon basin, closely guarded by their witch doctors . . .

As his physician talked on, the bedridden patient, homesick for his remote Ecuadorian ranch, pricked up his ears. A witch doctor! Maybe he could qualify! His Indian friends, to whom he had already demonstrated some modern man's tricks, already regarded him as something of a brujo. Surely he, if anyone, could persuade the Indian brujos to reveal their secrets. It wouldn't be easy, but it must be tried because of the thousands of sufferers who needed this help. For this, if for no other reason, he must get well.

As the slow months of recovery dragged by, Richard Gill began to make plans for an expedition into the jungle fastnesses. It must a well-equipped, well-staffed expedition; yet, because of problems of transportation, it must be small. Since it might well be a unique venture, they must go prepared to study the jungle and its inhabitants from as many angles as possible — botanical, zoological, pharmaceutical, and anthropological. They must seek out Indians who were practically untouched by contacts with outside civilizations, must live among them and prove to them and their brujos that the secret of curare might, without dangerously violating any ancient taboos, be shared with the white witch doctor. Not a small order!

Imagine, if you can, having to take everything you need for several months' living off into the depths of the forest. If later you find you have made errors, you cannot rectify them. Yet you must take as little as possible because everything has to be ready to go as manloads and boatloads. Food, clothes, ammunition, medical and surgical supplies, scientific equipment, trade goods — all these must be considered, item by item, so that no essential be overlooked and nothing that can be spared be included. Weeks later, in a remote jungle camp, the lack of anything important may well spell disaster for you and for your whole party.

Any old-timer in the expedition game will tell you that a good expedition — one that is carefully planned and efficiently executed — is not really an adventurous one. At least, it's not dangerously adventurous. You don't have hairbreadth escapes from this and that suddenly confronting menace if you plan right. A snake may attack you, though snakes are usually timid creatures unless threatened by danger, but you're a fool if you don't have antivenin close at hand. A boat overturns in the river! You should have planned for that and have packed everything water can damage in watertight tins.

Perhaps you have trouble with the Indians. You've probably offended them in some fundamental manner which you might have avoided if you had made the effort to acquaint yourself with their sacred taboos. Or maybe you've been found prying into secrets that are none of your business. Reticence, courtesy, respect for other people's time-honored beliefs and customs — if you remember these social rules here as in the drawing rooms at home, you probably won't have any real trouble with any of the strangers you meet.

Still and all, going into the jungle to persuade witch doctors to reveal their trade secrets is no matter for most seasoned explorers, even. It could be highly dangerous. Almost as bad would be having no chance to face the danger. For if the Indians suspect your motives or take a dislike to anything about you, they will simply disappear and all you will encounter will be deserted villages with, perhaps, still warm hearths to taunt you with their owners' recent departure. If they find you too unendurable, they can always settle the matter quickly and quietly with a poison-tipped pointed stick planted upright in the path you will have to tread. It needn't cause more than a slight scratch, remember.

In 1938, almost exactly a hundred years after the Schomburgk brothers had first witnessed a portion of the curare ritual in Guiana, the Gill-Merrill Ecuadorian Expedition set out from New York for Ecuador. They went from the port to a city in the high sierras where they put in three weeks completing their equipment with small local purchases and packing all their baggage in large tins so that each tin would make a manload and two could be balanced nicely over a mule's packsaddle. This completed, they set out for the ranch on the Rio Pastaza from which they would start on their jungle trek.

After a three days' journey, the mule trail came to an end and the Indians shouldered the loads while the mules returned to the ranch. It seemed then as if civilization had been finally and completely left behind. Ahead lay only narrow, dim, winding jungle trails where mud sucked at the men's feet and where lianas trailing down from the jungle giants clawed at the intruders. It was a treadmill where the scenery never altered and they seemed to make no progress at all.

After days on the jungle trail, they came at last and with delight to the banks of a river. Here, as arranged in advance, waited six dugout canoes with their boatmen — *bogas* — to take the party to its destination farther down the river. Here they would move more swiftly and more dangerously. The river had come a long way from the Andean heights where it had sprung. Between stretches of quiet water, it was still rushing along with headlong speed, boiling violently in rapids that foamed white across the boulder-strewn stream bed, roaring so deafeningly that, as Richard Spruce had once noted for other rivers of that region, they could be heard an hour before they were reached.

To take loaded boats through such waters required the most skilled of bogas. Already alerted by the sound, they watch keenly for the first line of foam. Seeing it, the leading boatman shouts a warning to those that follow while he drops his now useless paddle and, in one swift gesture, picks up the pole which he will use to hold his canoe away from the rocks, visible and invisible. The boga knows the channel, knows the risks, and knows his own skill. He keeps his head as the canoe shoots ahead, tilts crazily, buries its nose in the waves and ships water to a degree alarming to his passengers. Sharp granite boulders reach greedily for the boat's sides. Undisturbed, the boga gets the canoe through to still water where, for a brief triumphant moment, he pauses to rest and to watch his fellows bring their own canoes through to safety.

Again and again the experience is repeated. Days may be counted not in hours but in rapids passed. And each time, as the explorer watches his boatmen bending skillfully with each twist and turn of the canoes, keeping their footholds as if each had grown to be a part of his boat, he wonders how he dare hope his luck will hold. Even the fittest and best trained of men must tire under the constant strain and make some small fatal mistake.

What, he asks himself while considering this, can he spare from all the equipment? If given a choice, which canoe would he sacrifice to the greedy god of the river? Through his mind runs the carefully made inventory of supplies and the packing lists of the boxes each boat carries. He shakes his head sadly. Because he has planned well and there is nothing superfluous on his list, he knows there is nothing he can spare. Fuel, lamps, stoves, firearms, foodstuffs, clothes, trade goods, medicines, scientific equipment — if any of these remain in the river the expedition must fail.

Fortunately for the expedition and for the world outside, none of them did. At long last, they arrived safely at their destination: a jungle village situated not too far from the banks of the river. Close by the river was a charming white beach with a charming promontory above and overlooking it. Here, if he could get permission from the elders of the neighboring village, the director hoped to make camp. Boats could be tied up at the protected beach where, also, baths might be taken. But no one who knew the region would dream of setting up housekeeping so close to the water. The promontory would be the place for that. The frightening flood potential of the rivers of the Amazon basin has in no way diminished since Richard Spruce described them so graphically a century ago.

"We had barely resigned ourselves to sleep," he wrote of the early experience which taught him an unforgettable lesson of caution, "when the storm burst over us and the river almost simultaneously began to rise. Speedily the beach was overflowed, the Indians leaped into the canoes; the waters continued to rise with great rapidity, coming in on us every few minutes with a roaring surge which broke under the canoes in whirlpools, and dashed them against each other. . . . We held on, the Indians using all their efforts to prevent the canoes from being smashed by blows from each other or from the floating trees which now began to careen past like mad bulls. So dense was the gloom that we could see nothing, while we were deafened by the pelting rain, the roaring floods, and the crashing of the branches of the floating trees, as they rolled over or dashed against each other; but each lightning-flash revealed to us all the horrors of our position. Assuredly I had slight hopes of living to see the day . . . the rise during the night had been eighteen feet."

It would in no way do to take immediate possession of the promontory. Indians had always sought the patron's permission to camp on his land and now, when the tables were turned, he must seek theirs. So he approached the village chief — the *curaca* — and, by means of appropriate words and alluring trade goods, persuaded him not only to consent to the encampment but to give his co-operation in the construction of the camp. At the curaca's command, the men and women of his tribe cleared about one acre of land from the heaviest growth, and built the palm-thatched, split-bamboo-floored shelters which would be the expedition's headquarters.

Thus the first hurdle was passed. The most difficult was yet to come. It would take a great deal more than respectful words and desirable trade goods to secure the secret formula which was the expedition's main objective. You do not walk up to the head of any nation, great or small, and demand that he reveal to you his secret weapons — not if you're wise, that is. Of course, you can try your hand at spying if you think you're clever at it. But if the other fellow is cleverer, it may turn out unhealthy for you. No use, either, to try to buy the information from the man in the street. Even Sir Walter Raleigh, so long ago, knew that very few men in each tribe shared the tribal secret of curare making. As in all international dealings, good will is the key. Convince the other fellow you may be a worthy sharer of his secrets, that you aren't the kind of person to let them be used against him, and your battle is nearly won.

In the jungle, as in less remote parts of the world, negotiation takes time. It begins as the jungle dwellers subject the strangers to wary and thorough examination which the strangers must accept without visible protest. In due time, it is hoped, the Indians conclude that though their visitors may do strange and inexplicable things, they are otherwise quite harmless. So a cautious exchange of views begins; then, perhaps, demonstrations of skill. Finally comes the discussion of more important matters.

Sufficiently impressed with the alien white witch doctor's chemical sleight of hand and his earnest respect for their powers, the jungle witch doctors came to accept him as one of their select guild. To him, then, might be revealed the

secrets of their jungle drugs, including that of curare preparation. To him, also, might be shown the plants themselves. He
might be permitted to make collections of them — identifiable
collections which would fix all the ingredients of the contro-
versial brew. Later, on the outside, new methods of preparation might be tried and the essentials of the process sifted from
the trivial.

But now, on the inside, every detail of the ritual of jungle
magic must be treated with deadly seriousness. He must carefully learn the prescribed fasts, the things he might do, the
gestures he must make, the words he must or must not say
while the witch doctor's cauldron is bubbling. Not only did
the future of curare as a drug depend upon how skillfully he
conducted himself: the future of every member of the expedition might well be at stake. Anything less than the deepest
respect shown to the experienced brujos could spell death to
them all and deny to numberless persons on the outside the
help that curare might eventually bring.

Like his predecessors of a century ago, today's brujo begins
his preparation of curare with a trip into the jungle to gather
the necessary ingredients — the roots of one plant and the
bark of others, notably of a woody liana bearing the botanical
name *Chondrodendron*. His collections complete, the brujo
returns to some spot nearer home yet sufficiently remote from
the habitations of his tribesmen so that he may keep an un-
interrupted vigil while the brew — the *jambi* — boils. As in
the Guiana of Schomburgk's day, the Indian has already laid
out the clay pots he needs and firewood sufficient to keep
those pots boiling constantly until his work is finished and the
poison ready.

Yet the brujo knows that all these — the right ingredients,
the right pots, the right firewood, and the right methods of

boiling — will fail to secure him a good strong curare if he forgets for one moment any of the elaborate ritual that his father taught him. The food he eats, the liquid he drinks, the people he looks upon or who look upon him in the course of this ritual — all these matter just as much today as in centuries past. Though the precise rules may vary slightly from tribe to tribe and region to region, their importance is unvarying.

The brujo must keep away from home and family — especially from the women of his family — while the jambi is boiling. The presence of a woman can ruin everything. For several days before starting the ritual, he must have abstained from salt, from fermented liquor, and from the hot pepper he loves. During the very last day, he must take no food at all. If he fails in any of this, his curare will be weak and worthless.

The first day's work consists of beating the collected ingredients out — placing each on a flat stone and pounding it with a wooden mallet. Still fasting, he retires to the lean-to he has prepared for himself where he rests briefly. Early in the morning, he builds his fires, sets his pots in place, pours in just the right amount of water, and adds the ingredients according to custom.

Custom had comfortably decreed all this. But custom had never before faced them with the problem of what the presence of a white-skinned colleague might do to the brew. Even after they agreed to permit him to be present, they must have had grave secret doubts. So, knowing his Indians, Richard Gill knew that they might, in the last moment, try to find an honorable means of escape from the — to them — risky commitment.

As, one day, he sat waiting for the promised summons to the ritual of curare making, the expected brujo turned up with a face long with worry. That something was amiss could well be seen. It meant, undoubtedly, that the brujo would try to go back on his agreement. If he did, this could be the beginning of the end. Other witch doctors would learn of it, and soon they too would beg off.

The important thing, Gill saw, was not merely to get this particular specimen of curare but to make sure that the man did not get away with his planned refusal. All the suffering and planning and risks were to be compensated by securing curare from as many distinct sources as possible. Now, as the downcast young curare maker sat silent before him, he wondered if all curare research might not be facing complete failure.

"My heart burns low," the young man murmured gravely, "but I can make no jambi for you. I cannot continue the sacrifice or do the cooking until six moons have gone across the hills." His woman, he explained, had just given birth to a fine, strong man-child. To make the jambi now could cause his child to sicken and die. Everyone knew a father must wait six months or the magic of the jambi would cause his child to sicken and die. With a girl-child, now, he might have taken the risks. But a man-child, and his first . . . He shook his head sadly.

True enough, jungle witchcraft forbade the brew. But jungle witchcraft could be called upon to forbid almost anything a brujo did not wish to do. Others would find excuses, too, and the affairs of the expedition, previously going so well, would come to a complete end. Something must be done about it, and quickly.

The apprentice brujo listened quietly and thoughtfully. Then, offering Yasacama, the young brujo, a cigarette, he began: " 'For many moons before this among you, your people have known of me and of my words. My words among you have always been good, I think. As yet not one of you has told me that my words are false, or that the goods I offer you are poor in quality. The knives I bring you do not bend at the first cut; the cloth I bring you wears well upon your women; and my thought-magic also is true.' . . .

"It was the sort of talk an Indian likes to hear, and likes to make himself. Yasacama listened carefully and spat several times between his fingers. As long as he did that, I knew I was all right.

"Then I handed him a peppermint Life-Saver . . . and told him that if he would put that in his mouth as soon as he lit his cooking fires, the magic of the jambi could not possibly harm his man-child.

"He looked at the round white mint for a moment . . . then he rose abruptly and said that he would make the jambi and use my magic, and that I should come to his cooking place early the next morning. As he was leaving, he looked directly at me and said, 'But, friend, it will not be good for you if my man-child travels in the Death canoe.' Then he left."*

So, sucking on the Life-Saver, Yasacama lit his cooking fires and began the preparation of the jambi. His white colleague sat close by, weighing each of the ingredients before it went into the pot, recording every detail of the process.

While the pot was boiling, one of Yasacama's brothers slipped silently into the little clearing, whispered a few words to Yasacama, and departed as silently as he had come. Yasacama looked Richard Gill in the eye and told him gravely the news his brother had brought. His man-child had sickened.

"It is the magic of the jambi," he explained, "for he was strong and well before I lit these fires. But I have the taste of your magic still in my mouth, and I shall continue to make the poison for you. But it will not be good for you if my man-child dies." *

His companion handed him another Life-Saver and said nothing. There was nothing he could say, for he understood only too well what might happen if Yasacama's baby died. Yet it was too late to turn back even had he wished to do so. While the fires burned bright, and the brew in the great clay pots simmered and Yasacama's brother returned again and again in menacing silence, bringing news that the baby was growing steadily weaker, the white witch doctor had to maintain perfect poise, to show absolute confidence in the power of his own magic.

"At the end of the third day, the curare came to its 'point'," he wrote, "and, still saying nothing, Yasacama poured it into the brown sun-cured gourd he had ready for it. When he was just about to deliver it to me, his brother came into the clearing again, and once more whispered to him. As always, he left as quickly as he came and without looking at me.

"Then Yasacama spoke for the first time in a long while. . . . He handed me the gourd of curare, which was still hot, and said, 'Your magic has been good. My man-child is not sick now. He will live. It is not according to the words of my fathers that any magic is stronger than the jambi. Now I have learned a new thing. Your magic and your words are good. Also, I like the taste of your magic in my mouth.' "*

The news spread up and down the jungle trails. Here was a man with a magic more powerful than any the Old Ones had ever known, a man to be helped in every way; a colleague who might be introduced to the most secret bits of jungle lore,

---

* From Gill's book, *White Water and Black Magic*.

who might be shown every detail of the jambi. So Richard Gill was able to take home with him the botanical specimens needed to identify with certainty the plants that went into curare as well as some other valuable jungle drugs. Moreover, he secured more curare of more kinds than anyone on the outside had ever dreamed could exist. And all because he had had the courage and will power to stake so much on the frail life of a jungle baby.

It was, of course, only the beginning of the story of curare. For botanical explorers would get to work to locate related plants that might be used for preparing the drug. The question of finding cultivable species would also come up. Pharmacologists could now study the effects of curare more extensively and more scientifically than had been possible before. Physicians and surgeons and anesthesiologists would apply the knowledge. Chemists would isolate the active principles and learn how they might be synthesized. If they would not be less costly than those from the jungle they would, at least, be less hazardous to secure.

Today, then, we have not just the arrow poison with its history of romance and adventure and terror. We have the chemical compound, d-tubocurarine, the first but surely not the last of the active curare principles to come out of the laboratory — literally a life-saving material from the ancient flying death.

X

A Look Ahead

PLANTS, whether bacteria or jungle giants, are living individuals and may alter in appearance and habits just as may the men who seek them. The plants that now are successfully grown for crops still live wild in the areas from which men first brought the seeds or cuttings. It may happen that the cultivated crops fail. Plant diseases may invade and threaten them with extinction. Or men may want to grow the crops in areas that require hardier plants than any they now know. Then they remember the wild plants that have learned how to survive in the free-for-all struggle of field or forest. In the wilds must be sought hardy and disease-resistant strains to interbreed with and give strength to the cultivated varieties. It was to northern Asia men went to seek the hardy wheat that can endure cold, and resist the inroads of wheat rust, upon which Canada's great wheat crop now depends.

Plant products, whether in commerce or medicine, have at last come into their own. Doctors, chemists, manufacturers are no longer scornful of the lessons plants can teach — lessons which they have long since taught the unsophisticated men of the wilds. Scientists of today listen with open minds to even quite fantastic folklore.

Somewhere in a remote settlement in Costa Rica lives an ignorant native herb doctor who, apparently competent eye-witnesses say, has brought back to health a man dying from the venom of the deadly bushmaster snake. Is it fact or illusion? What did the herb doctor use? The herb doctor shrugs his shoulders and reveals no professional secrets, though if you wish his services you may have them for a small fee. Someday someone is going to get to the bottom of all this. Doctor or chemist — whoever starts the investigation, the plant hunter well may have the last word.

In other areas of the same land, natives cheerfully cure themselves of arthritis by drinking a not unpleasant decoction of the leaves of a *Cassia* plant they call "sarangundine." Study medieval herbals and you will find that even then *Cassia* species were recommended for their curative properties. Today the physician who barely twenty years ago refused to put sarangundine to the test has learned all about those plant-produced curative substances we call "antibiotics." If it were recommended, he'd be glad to try the cassic acid which laboratory experiments have shown to be an active principle of the once rejected plant.

As both Sir Robert Talbor and Dr. John Sappington recognized so long ago, there may be a very great deal in a name. "Cassic acid" has that modern scientific sound which "sarangundine" lacks. Someday, perhaps, generations of bacteria immune to presently available antibiotics may develop. We will then have to find new antibiotics with which the bacteria are as yet unfamiliar. Then it may be that *Cassia* species will come into their own. Who knows?

Sometimes the plant we need is well known and the use to which it is put generally accepted. The question may become, can we find a substitute plant and where? For many lands, remembering how South America lost both its rubber and its quinine monopolies, have tried to prevent a repetition of the story in their own cases. If the plant product is of vital importance, though, men will find a way of getting it, embargo or no embargo.

The herb doctors of India have used for many centuries a drug prepared from a small woody plant that grows wild almost everywhere in India. They claimed for the plant such remarkable powers that for a long time European doctors dismissed it all as ignorant, superstitious quackery.

It was natural that this particular plant should be included in a book written about the useful and otherwise remarkable plants of the Spice Islands. In 1653, one Georg Eberhardt Rumpff was sent out by the Dutch East India Company to compile such a book and it was he who made the first botanical drawing of the plant that in our own century was to gain wide interest under the name *Rauwolfia*. Tragedy haunted Rumpff, whose life's work was not completed until 1701, a few months before his death. It was not published until nearly a half century later.

There, buried in Rumpff's book, Western knowledge of *Rauwolfia* rested for nearly two centuries more. Indian herb doctors continued to use the plant and, impressed by what it seemed to do, Indian scientists finally became interested in studying the drug. In 1931 two chemists of India isolated five active alkaloids from *Rauwolfia* plants. Two years later three of their fellow countrymen began publication of a series of studies of the effects of these alkaloids upon high blood pressure. Since high blood pressure was then becoming one of the acute medical problems of an overcivilized world, the scientifically demonstrated effectiveness of *Rauwolfia* alkaloids against such "hypertension" was greeted with eager interest. This was the beginning of many of our tranquilizing drugs.

Naturally the demand for *Rauwolfia* plants increased by leaps and bounds. And as demand grew, natives hastened to gather and sell for profit every one of the plants they could lay their hands upon. The plant that once had been found everywhere began to grow scarce. Efforts to cultivate it were quietly made while the Indian government, alarmed lest its *Rauwolfia* monopoly go the way of Brazilian rubber, placed an embargo upon exportation of the plant.

Fortunately for the rest of the world, *Rauwolfia* is not the name of a single plant species but of that larger group, called "genus," which may include many species. Consulted in the matter, a botanist could point out that while *Rauwolfia serpentina* seemed to belong to India and thereabouts, there was *Rauwolfia tetraphylla,* also a small woody shrub, that grew in Mexico and Central America. In the Belgian Congo grows a *Rauwolfia* tree, *Rauwolfia vomitoria.*

Did these related species produce related alkaloids? Chemists set to work to extract the active principles. Pharmacologists tested those principles and found them about as effective as the drug prepared from the Indian *Rauwolfia.* And there, if they so wish, experts in tropical horticulture may take up the task of learning how to cultivate the plants.

We see again that the profession of plant hunting can never become out of date. As old as man, as new as the latest scientific discovery, it is bound to appeal to many men. The excitement of adventure in remote places, the excitement of discovery, the excitement of adding to human knowledge, increasing human comfort, lessening human misery — all these combine to lure men of many backgrounds to the fascinating work.

And so we close this account of some of the more important plants that have changed the world. Even if we could deal with all the plants that men have already come to depend upon, we could never really end the story.

Bibliography

PUBLISHER'S NOTE: *The starred titles are probably available in most larger libraries and will interest young people for further reading.*

CAMERON, HECTOR CHARLES. *Sir Joseph Banks, K.B., F.R.S., the autocrat of the philosophers.* London: The Batchworth Press, 1952. xx & 341 pp. illus.

COOK, JAMES. *The voyage of the Endeavour, 1768-1771.* Ed. J.C. Beaglehole. Cambridge, Eng.: The Hakluyt Society, 1955. cclxxxiv & 684 pp.

*DURAN-REYNALS, MARIE LOUISE. *The fever bark tree. The pageant of quinine.* New York: Doubleday & Co., 1946. xi & 175 pp.

*EDWARDS, H. T. The introduction of abacá (Manila hemp) into the western hemisphere. *Annual Report of the Board of Regents of the Smithsonian Institution.* . . . Publ. 3817. 1945: 327-350. 10 pl.

ERNEHOLM, IVAR. *Cacao production of South America; historical development and present geographical distribution.* Inaug. diss. Gothenburg. 1948. 279 pp.

GAGE, THOMAS. *Nueva relación que contient los viajes de Tomás Gage en la Nueva España.* . . . 1625. Biblioteca "Goathemala," Vol. XVIII, 1946.

GILL, RICHARD C. *White water and black magic.* New York: Henry Holt & Co., 1940. xiv & 369 pp. illus.

GILL, RICHARD C. Curare: misconceptions regarding its discovery and development of the present form of the drug. *Anesthesiology,* 7:14-23, 1946.

*HAGEN, VICTOR WOLFGANG VON. *South America called them. Explorations of the great naturalists La Condamine, Humboldt,*

Darwin, Spruce. New York: Alfred A. Knopf, 1945. xii & 312 pp. & ix. illus.

HUMBOLDT, A. VON, and BONPLAND, A. *Voyage aux régions équi-noctiales du nouveau continent. Relation historique du voyage.* Translated by Thomasina Rose. London: George Bell & Sons, 1881-85. 3 vols.

*KNAGGS, NELSON S. *Adventures in man's first plastic. The romance of natural waxes.* New York: Reinhold Publishing Corp., 1947. xiv & 329 pp. illus.

MCINTYRE, ARCHIBALD ROSS. *Curare; its history, nature and clinical use.* Chicago: Univ. Chicago Press, 1947. vii & 240 pp. illus.

*MORISON, SAMUEL ELIOT. *The maritime history of Massachusetts, 1783-1860.* Boston: Houghton Mifflin Co., 1921. xvii & 401 pp.

MORISON, SAMUEL ELIOT. *The ropemakers of Plymouth. A history of the Plymouth Cordage Company, 1824-1949.* Boston: Houghton Mifflin Co., 1950. vi & 177 pp.

RALEIGH, WALTER. *The discoverie of the large, rich and bewtiful empire of Guiana performed in the year 1595.* Ed. Robert Schomburgk. London: The Hakluyt Society, 1848. lxxv, xv, & 240 pp.

REMESAL, FRAY ANTONIO DE. *Historia general de las Indias occidentales y particular de la gobernación de Chiapa y Guatemala.* 1619. Reprinted in Biblioteca "Goathemala," Vols. IV & V, 1932.

*ROBINSON, B. B., and JOHNSON, F. L. *Abacá, a cordage fiber.* Agriculture Monograph No. 21. U.S. Dept. Agr. Beltsville, Md., Oct. 1953. 130 pp.

*ROCK, JOSEPH H. *The chaulmoogra tree and some related species: a survey conducted in Siam, Burma, Assam, and Bengal.* U.S. Dept. Agr. Bull. 1057: 1-29, 1922. 16 pl.

*ROCK, JOSEPH H. Hunting the chaulmoogra tree. *National Geographic Mag.,* 41:242-276, 1922.

*RUSBY, HENRY H. *Jungle memories.* New York: McGraw-Hill Book Co., 1933. xiii & 388 pp. illus.

SCHOMBURGK, RICHARD. *Botanical reminiscences in British Guiana.* Adelaide, Australia: W. C. Cox, 1876. 90 pp.

SCHOMBURGK, RICHARD. *On the urari: the deadly arrow poison of the Macusis, an Indian tribe in British Guiana.* Adelaide, 1879.

SCHOMBURGK, ROBERT. On the urari, the arrow poison of the Indians of Guiana, with a description of the plant from which it is extracted. *Ann. Mag. Nat. Hist.,* I Ser., 7:407-427, 1841.

SPRUCE, RICHARD. *Notes of a botanist on the Amazon and Andes....* London: Macmillan & Co., Ltd., 1908. 2 vols.

SUPPAN, LEO. Three centuries of cinchona. *Proc. Celebration 300th Ann. 1st Recognized Use of Cinchona,* 29-138, 1931.

TERRY, ROBERT J. Dr. John Sappington, pioneer in the use of quinine in the Mississippi valley. *Proc. Celebration 300th Ann. 1st Recognized Use Cinchona,* 165-180, 1931.

WATERTON, CHARLES. *Wanderings in South America.* London: Macmillan & Co., 1879. vii & 341 pp.

WICKHAM, HENRY ALEXANDER (Sir). *Rough notes on a journey through the wilderness.* . . . London: W. H. J. Carter, 1872. xv & 301 pp. illus.

WICKHAM, HENRY ALEXANDER (Sir). *On the plantation, cultivation, and curing of Pará rubber (Hevea brasiliensis).* London: Kegan Paul, Trench, Trübner & Co., Ltd., 1908. 78 pp. illus.

*WILSON, CHARLES MORROW. *Trees and test tubes, the story of rubber.* New York: Henry Holt & Co., 1943. xii & 352 pp.

WOODSON, ROBERT E., JR., YOUNGKEN, HEBER W., SCHLITTLER, E., and SCHNEIDER, JURG A. *Rauwolfia: botany, pharmacognosy, chemistry and pharmacology.* Boston: Little, Brown & Co., 1956. x & 149 pp.

Index